Hyper-Beings:

How Intelligent Organizations Attain Supremacy through Information Superiority

Dr. Rick Hayes-Roth[1]

Information Sciences Department,
Naval Postgraduate School,
Monterey, CA

[1] Dr. Hayes-Roth is Professor, Information Sciences, Naval Postgraduate School, Monterey, CA. He may be reached via email at: hayes-roth@nps.edu.

Hyper-Beings:

How Intelligent Organizations Attain Supremacy through Information Superiority

Dr. Rick Hayes-Roth

Table of Contents

About the Author

Rick Hayes-Roth is currently a professor in the Information Sciences Department at the Naval Postgraduate School in Monterey, California. At NPS he teaches the "capstone" course on strategy and policy in exploiting information technology. Prior to joining the NPS faculty, he was the Chief Technology Officer for Software at Hewlett-Packard. Before that he was Chairman and Chief Executive of two Silicon Valley companies which he co-founded. He was the program director for research in Information Processing at The Rand Corporation and, prior to that, was one of the co-inventors of the first continuous speech understanding systems, Hearsay-II, which became the ubiquitous "blackboard architecture."

Dr. Hayes-Roth has written more than 100 published papers and co-authored three other books, *Building Expert Systems, Pattern-Directed Inference System,* and *Radical Simplicity: Transforming Computers into Me-Centric Appliances.* He's held faculty positions at MIT, Stanford, and Carnegie Mellon, as well as NPS. He's a Fellow of the American Association for Artificial Intelligence, a Senior Member of the IEEE, and a member of the Association for Computing Machinery.

Dr. Hayes-Roth is an avid private pilot and commutes by air from Palo Alto to Monterey in a single-engine Piper Dakota. He's been married to Barbara Hayes-Roth since their graduate school days, and they have three children.

Preface

This book may alarm you. It describes a new state of nature, not yet fully evident, that I see coming soon to our planet. The dominant beings in this emerging environment are neither animals, nor plants, nor mechanical whirligigs. Rather, they are human-machine hybrids that spread their tentacles over thousands of miles. They communicate at the speed of light, and they conquer their opponents through a combination of superior intelligence and physical precision. I call these creatures *hyper-beings,* because they have the focused intent of a unified being yet possess physical and intellectual dimensions vastly exceeding those of all previous life forms. Hyper-beings are the naturally selected dominant forms of a world unified by intelligent information systems. These systems enable hyper-beings to operate as if borders did not exist. These systems exploit ever-increasing capabilities in computing, communication, and information processing to achieve unprecedented levels of awareness and physical reach. As with other technological revolutions, if channeled and governed wisely, these new capabilities can yield great benefits. On the other hand, if misunderstood or misdirected, they can run amok and threaten global well-being.

I am, mostly, a technophile and optimist. I think that hyper-beings can lift humanity to new levels of wealth and well-being, if we design them well, administer them reasonably, and govern them responsibly. So my principal goals are to help more people participate in this revolution, to hasten the opportunities, and to help avert some predictable problems. To assure that the anticipated changes improve human welfare, rather than diminish it, we will need to inform people about the coming changes and stimulate appropriate political dialogue, policy-making and social engineering. I hope this book ignites readers' creative energies. We need creativity in two complementary spheres. First, we want to accelerate the development of these extraordinary intelligent creatures so they can produce for us better, faster and cheaper goods and services. At the same time, because hyper-beings compete supremely well and naturally rise to dominate vast arenas, we must invent improved mechanisms of transnational, post-industrial governance as a check against unbridled power and extreme imbalances in economic conditions.

I first coined the term *hyper-being* while participating in a special "Bold Ideas" group established by and for the support of Marv Langston, who was in 1998-2000 the Deputy Chief Information Officer of the U.S. Department of Defense, under the Assistant Secretary of Defense for Command, Control,

Communications and Intelligence, Art Money. Dr. Langston formerly directed DARPA's Information System Office, the group responsible for creating radical new possibilities to enhance DoD's performance through superior use of information technology. DARPA, the Defense Advanced Research Projects Agency, had famously brought other revolutionary technologies to fruition, including the Internet, artificial intelligence, massively parallel computers, and autonomous aircraft and robots. The US Government has demonstrated repeatedly that patient, focused, visionary R&D yields extraordinary results. The Bold Ideas group surveyed the landscape and pretty quickly determined that hyper-beings would produce the next revolution in the arena of powerful players on the world stage.

The context for the group's work included a recognition in the '90s at DoD of the need for a "revolution in military affairs" (RMA). The contemplated RMA recognized that the US and its allies would become involved in a widening range of conflicts and needed a new approach to make this affordable and effective. One key goal was to exploit our superior technology to enable our forces' to perform excellently over the entire spectrum of engagements, from peace-keeping and humanitarian relief at one extreme to hot conflicts in major battlefield theaters at the other. Everyone recognized that a new asymmetry existed. The US has huge physical and technological advantages, but threats to security would come from an expanded range of actors, expected increasingly to be non-nation-states. Nation states, tied as they are to physical assets, wealth, and infrastructure, are sitting ducks in conflicts with superior forces. Natural selection would quickly weed out such opponents. Natural selection, at the same time, would favor challengers who could operate "below the radar" so to speak, diffusely, without fixed physical structures. Thus, by envisioning how competition would play out, it was clear that opponents to US hegemony would need to take amorphous forms, move continuously, and operate outside the networks and channels easily controlled and monitored by the US and its allies.

But what form would US power take, and would the answer differ for military organizations versus commercial ones? Assuming that technology would continue its rapid rate of progress, that competitive pressures would operate, could we foresee the shape of dominant beings that would emerge? Could we help assure that these superior beings would be on our side and not on the side of terrorists and despots? These questions led to our recognizing the emergence of hyper-beings. Once we had the concept and knew what to look for, we found evidence supporting the hypothesis nearly everywhere.

This book aims to share those insights and explain the principal mechanisms at work. Even without directly teaching the details of technology to implement hyper-beings, I expect the reader to get the big picture and begin to perceive the everyday events confirming these major ideas. Many readers I expect will then start adapting to the changed circumstances so they find ways to prosper and, hopefully, keep out of the tar pits[2].

I've written this book with several different sorts of readers in mind. First, this book addresses the modern intellectual who wishes to understand enough about technology and its effects on social evolution to participate knowingly. Participation can range from creative roles in developing and implementing the technology, to management and investment in associated businesses, to leadership roles in industry, government or non-governmental organizations. This book will provide enough information and understanding to give these readers what they need so they can directly participate in shaping the future. Second, the book aims at students of the key areas, including intelligent systems and post-industrial management and organization. There's a lot of business to be done with hyper-beings, and this book enables the student to understand the required fundamentals. I expect this book belongs in computer science, information systems, business administration, military science and public policy curricula. The third group of readers I hope to address includes military officers and contractors, who provide our service personnel the doctrine, tactics, training, and systems to do their jobs. These people must race to implement the concepts in this book, so our armed forces and civil security agencies rise to the highest levels of performance, as quickly as possible.

I'd like to acknowledge the many colleagues and sponsors I've worked with over the years whose support has made it possible for me to develop these ideas. My colleagues at MIT Sloan School of Management, Carnegie Mellon Department of Computer Science, The Rand Corporation, Teknowledge Corp., DARPA, and the Naval Postgraduate School are too numerous to name individually. Each of these institutions provided me time to think, quality colleagues to work with, and patient capital to bring difficult

---

[2] In Los Angeles, the La Brea Tar Pits hold remains of many formerly great dinosaurs that became stuck in tar while looking for water. As the environment becomes less hospitable, each creature incurs increased risks as it moves out of well known "comfort zones" that previously provided viable habitat. If the environment changes extensively and quickly, only highly adaptable critters survive.

ideas to fruition. I hope this book reflects well on them and brings many dividends to their current and future faculty, students, engineers, and policy analysts. I feel incredibly lucky to have lived through the early decades of the information revolution, and I'm confident that we've collectively not seen anything yet!

1. Introduction: The Big Picture

Working smarter beats working harder. This aphorism reveals much about our competitive world and how it has evolved from earlier times when physical mass, size, and strength determined the success of individuals, enterprises, and military forces. Labor, capital, and know-how constitute the three big ingredients in almost any organization. The relative importance of these varies over time, reflecting changes in supply and changes in technology. For the last twenty years at least, technology has been changing rapidly, while both labor and capital remained relatively plentiful. Technology is related to all three big inputs, but is most directly tied in contemporary settings to the know-how factor. New technology means one group can do things another group cannot, because it possesses enabling know-how. Especially as such know-how becomes embedded in computer software, machines and appliances, we can easily replicate and deploy it widely. Further, as time intervals required for innovating, decision-making, and deploying new ideas continue to shrink, working smarter requires knowing more valuable things, having access to better information, and making better decisions faster than competitors can. In short, working smarter means thinking better thoughts and implementing them better, faster and cheaper than others can.

Superior information enables better decisions. Life is full of possibilities, and these usually manifest themselves as choices we must make. Usually, we can opt to "do nothing," which means not intervening to change the situation, or we can elect to perform one or more actions. Obviously, we want to choose alternatives that give us the best possible outcome, in our own terms. This is usually termed "optimizing the expected outcome." To optimize, we must act to get the best possible result. This requires that we execute actions that we believe probably will yield better outcomes than any other action we might perform. To do this, we combine our knowledge of "the way things work" with information that tells us "the current state of affairs."

For example, we may believe that rain in the early afternoon usually means it will rain at 4:30 pm. Thus, if we learn that it is raining at 2 pm, we believe that it will probably rain at 4:30 pm. This inference combines our predictive models with our current situation assessment to produce an expectation of the future situation. If we will be meeting a friend at 4:30 pm, we prudently propose an indoor meeting place in preference to an outside location. We expect that action to keep us from getting unhappily wet. Of course, the quality of our decision-making depends directly upon the quality of the information we receive. Accurate information about rain in the early afternoon is valuable, because it enables us to employ our somewhat primitive model of how things work. Even better information would be possible, if we or others were able to employ it to infer more accurate predictions. A detailed meteorological simulation of the local area might give much better predictions and, in that case, using that information would enable us to consider more options and perhaps reach a superior decision.

Information-superior organizations prevail. People do most of their work as part of organizations, whether their employers, volunteer organizations, clubs or families. Organizations, like individuals, compete in a world of scarce resources occupied by a population of hungry competitors. Organizations make and implement decisions that determine the organizations' outcomes. Obviously, organizations that get better information and use it more effectively than others have a major competitive advantage. Although a few exceptions might arise, organizations that intelligently employ superior information beat their competitors. As a short-hand, I refer to these as *information-superior* organizations. Information-superior organizations reach better decisions and implement them more effectively than mediocre organizations. They have what business people and military leaders often wish for: *an unfair advantage.* When conditions persist, the information-superior organization surpasses existing competitors, prevails against challengers, and attains supremacy in its dominion. Because organizations control the preponderance of the world's resources and activities, the information-superior organizations reign supreme over our planet. If these were living creatures, we'd surely perceive them as a dominant species.

Organizations comprise mostly hierarchical, information-based, distributed components. We are all familiar with organizations that disperse employees and work sites widely over one or more geographic regions. This dispersion corresponds to *physical* distribution. But organizations also routinely distribute vital functions, such as *decision-making* and *control.* Information collected in various locales finds its way to groups and decision-makers around the globe that need it. Each local entity makes some decisions, passes its plans and results along to other parts of the organization, and higher management integrates, interprets, and assesses these results as part of its own decision-making processes. Decisions, plans, results, and observations flow around the distributed organization.

2

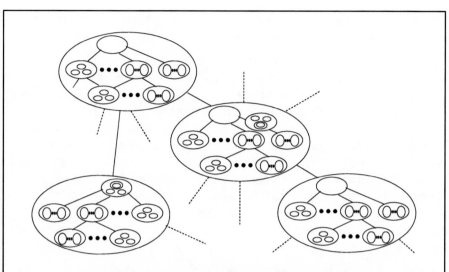

Figure 1. Holons in a holarchic organization.

Each holon is an entity that comprises components and yet presents a single unified interface to external entities. The internal components may themselves be organizations of holons. Holarchies, which are hierarchies of holons, permit us to architect organizations of great complexity using a minimum of communication.

Arthur Koestler coined the term *holon* to describe a self-contained decision-making entity that both contains suborganizations and participates as a component of a larger or higher-order organization [1]. Holonic organizations are *self-similar* or *fractal*, meaning that their basic compositional structure repeats at every level of aggregation or scale. Within any holonic organization, holons at every level perform identical types of information-processing tasks. A holon receives goals and guidance from its superiors; it assesses the situation so that it can evaluate alternative actions and implement the most desirable ones; and, in turn, it directs its subordinates to do their parts to achieve the intended results. Organizations manifest various important aspects. They construct and populate physical and formal structures. They adopt and follow polices and procedures. They develop and sustain values and cultural norms. But the information that the organization communicates and processes provides its lifeblood. Because the other factors change very slowly, if at all, recent and current information effectively determines what the organization actually does. Absent current and correct information, the organization acts like a senseless animal.

Distributed intelligent organizations exploiting information superiority become *hyper-beings*. We live in a world where intelligent life forms have broken free of their purely physical, terrestrial legacy. The Internet, as a prime example, has created thousands of virtual "places" and "worlds" where real and virtual characters interact. The World Wide Web has become the world's biggest and most frequented library, with people looking to the web first to find answers to everyday questions. Intelligent organizations use all of these technologies, and others, to enable themselves to collect better information, to analyze it more thoroughly, to conjecture and evaluate alternative courses of action, to choose and implement their plans, to coordinate and control their agents and resources, and to monitor, feed back, and adapt to experienced outcomes.

From a sufficiently distant vantage point, we might not discern individual agents and resources participating in any such plan. We might only see the observable effects or what social scientists on Earth would term the organization's "behavior." We would then perceive how these distributed intelligent organizations exploit their information superiority to affect the world. We would be watching hyper-beings showing off their special talent. We would observe distributed organizations, composed of holons, efficiently and effectively collecting and processing information, dynamically adapting their goals and behaviors to attain and sustain supremacy.

You need to understand and apply some of these fundamental lessons in your own life. The principles that dominant organizations employ matter to you for several reasons. First, you probably participate in a range of organizations that vary in their capability to exploit these new technologies and methods. You can probably help your organizations attain superior results by evolving their processes and methods. You can identify impediments to information superiority and work to eliminate them. You can alter strategies to take account of the new competitive landscape. You can help conceive and implement more appropriate and effective systems to support the distributed intelligent decision-making hyper-beings need. Furthermore, as new products and services come to market, you can employ these to improve outcomes in the organizations you participate in. Learning the basic steps of intelligent decision-making and continually improving the tools you employ to support it will go a long way toward making you more productive and successful.

Competition is ubiquitous, so rewards go disproportionately to those that prevail. Economists perceive competition as a natural response to scarcity, a chafing constraint in the quantity of goods and services available for consumption. The scarce resource might be housing, beachfront property, new cars, or whatever. The world simply doesn't have as many of these available as the total amount desired by all the people on earth. Thus, people and organizations compete to get more of these goods at lower costs than others can. So everyone has to compete for scarce resources, but some organizations excel at it and obtain better results than others do.

In the biological world, we measure success by population size and reproductive rates. Humans have been doing very well in these terms lately, though the experiences of individual humans vary widely. Affluent citizens of the developed countries are getting more and better valued goods than others do. Similarly, some of the business organizations are earning more profits than others. Furthermore, some military organizations, notably that of the US and members of NATO, have been deriving better outcomes for their efforts than others have. In all of these arenas, rewards accrue disproportionately to those on the top of the heap. In competition, out-thinking and out-implementing others means you take home much more than they do.

Combining technologies for information superiority and distributed intelligence with capabilities for effective action produces supremacy. The computing field is about 60 years old. For the entire period of its development, the field has been racing ahead with new innovations, more powerful capabilities, and better-faster-cheaper computing and communication devices. The rate these technologies have evolved is without precedent in the worlds of engineering or biology. As a result of Moore's Law, we have computing devices that double in capacity every 18 months. As a result of similar improvements in communication, networking, and Internet software techniques, we see an exponential increase in the number of computers, megabytes of stored and processed information, and human-machine interactions.

In spite of all of these accomplishments, we are still early in the history of hyper-beings and their competitive evolution. We can already see that organizations have transformed to exploit opportunities available through information superiority. Enterprises have radically altered their supply chains, manufacturing processes, and distribution systems to cut huge amounts of time and cost from their products. Dell computing and Federal Express package delivery companies are often cited as stellar examples of these approaches. But most companies have not radically altered the way they do business yet, nor has the military accomplished the significant transformations its leaders seek. In the next decade, we will witness many organizations make the bold moves required to become information-superior hyper-beings. Some of these will fail. Others will prevail, attaining positions of supremacy they should be able to sustain indefinitely.

Many technological and doctrinal trends support the impending transformations. Computing power increases and costs decrease on a regular basis. A single PC today has more computing power than most laboratories and research facilities had 25 years ago. In the next 10 years, individuals will be able to purchase for a few thousand dollars personal supercomputers, capable of computing the most challenging algorithms currently known. Organizations with thousands of computers, will find these interconnected by the Internet or its successor, providing vast bandwidth for real-time collaboration and information sharing. Every organization will be seeking ways to increase its information superiority, and few will find themselves limited by computing or communication resources. Instead, they will be limited by the rate they can adopt and implement the systems and practices required to unleash intelligent hyper-being behavior. Specifically, they will need to understand what structures and processes foster this behavior, how to implement those, and how to adapt them over time to improve. The speed with which they implement these information-superior capabilities and the rate at which they adapt and evolve them will determine the organization's velocity through the competitive terrain. Information-superior hyper-beings will leave unexceptional competitors in the dust. They will accrue advantages that make them seem alien to this world. They will see further, foresee farther, envision more, plan more creatively and effectively, and implement more efficiently than any creature or enterprise our world has ever known.

Hyper-beings constitute the dominant species of the new world order. The physical world and the cyber-world occupy two segments of one true world. In the physical world, we interact with molecules and experience mass. We mine things, fabricate them, ship them, consume them, and ultimately destroy them. This is the only world known to our ancestors. In the cyber-world, a world of information processing, we manipulate bits, words, packets, files, objects and streams. These bits bear information and *mean* something when we interpret them in the context of our beliefs and expectations. We use *models* to understand how the world works. The models are mostly intuitive and informal, although in some cases we use formal or computational models, as when we simulate the weather to forecast it or simulate a nuclear weapon explosion to evaluate its performance.

When sensor observations, news reports, business results, and intelligence analyses reach us, we determine the "news" or "information" content by determining whether and how what we are receiving differs from what we already know or believe. No matter how many times someone may tell us something that we already know, the redundant reports have no information value. On the other hand, when information doesn't accord with our beliefs, that is news, and it's always an opportunity to learn something new. Further, if our beliefs change, it may be necessary to change on-going behavior or revise plans, because the new information wasn't available when the plan was chosen as the most desirable alternative.

So information reflects what's occurring in the world and causes us to change our behavior to re-optimize it in light of our best, most up-to-date models of how the world works. Hyper-beings, possessing the best information collection, modeling, information analysis, planning and control resources, can put more resources to work optimizing and re-optimizing their behaviors. Their size and resources are advantages in this game. Those who master the information processing challenges and apply their improved thing with effective action will dominate. In this new world, where physical and cyber-realties intertwine, hyper-beings become the predominant species.

This book attempts to anticipate and help shape the rise of hyper-beings. In this first part, I describe hyper-beings and their principal characteristics. This provides a big picture of the emerging landscape to make its principal features evident. Readers should comprehend how hyper-beings organize, communicate, coordinate, and behave. They should perceive their comparative advantages. They should feel they understand where this evolutionary line has come from and where it's headed.

I think it's no exaggeration to say that our computing and communication technologies are combining to constitute a transformational force on humanity as great as those as fire and the written word. Fire enabled people to vastly extend their habitat, in terms of distance, climate, and daily hours. Fire enabled us to eat more and different things, and ultimately to create fearsome weapons and precision tools. The written word also extended the range and reach of humanity. In this case, writing allowed people to transmit know-how from one place to many others, accelerating the diffusion and advance of culture. In a similar way, the ability of contemporary organizations to organize at various levels of aggregation, to work at appropriate levels of abstraction, to observe globally, to communicate at the speed of light, to test and evolve models, to plan and control precisely the activities of thousands or millions of distributed cooperating components exponentially expands the scope of human activity and the grasp of organizations. I see no natural limit to the size and scale of this grasp. Rather, as in earlier industrial days, hyper-beings have natural economies of scale: the bigger they get, the more efficient, effective, and naturally dominant they become. Hyper-beings want to include more parties, co-opt others into their systems, and collectively control more of the world. That which they do not control, they cannot optimize.

Are hyper-beings good or bad? Although hackneyed, we ought to judge people, organizations and cyber-beings by what they do rather than what technology they employ. Science and technology repeatedly offer us opportunities to do good or evil. We have organizations today that do good and others that do evil. We have some governments on Earth that do good and others that do evil. There's no doubt that hyper-beings will be the most powerful, intelligent, farthest reaching entities ever known. Their potential can't be overstated. The opportunity for abuse of power is apparent. Undoubtedly, we will need to create new means of checks-and-balances to assure that the enormous power of these new creatures doesn't run amok. At the same time, hyper-beings will attain levels of efficiency and effectiveness that can produce great benefits to their customers, investors, partners and participants. In optimistic pursuit of that positive potential, I invite the reader to step into Chapter 2, where we make evident the radical nature of the changes afoot.

2. "We're not in Kansas anymore"

Depending on when you grew up, life was simpler in many ways. Just a few generations ago, people grew up without TV and cell phones. Many people now living reached adulthood before they touched a computer or videogame. Today's teens have grown up with PCs, the Internet, WiFi wireless networks, the web, file sharing, and many other technologies that have disrupted the slow pace of life in the 20th century. Well, in the words of a familiar spokesperson, get ready now for something entirely different.

We have left the world of autonomy, independence, and local business behind, for good. These qualities were valuable when a person's reach was severely constrained by limited physical resources, limited transportation capabilities, and weak information processing technology. When making money required moving molecules, people had to locate their activities close to resources, distribution centers, and customers. This proximity gave an advantage to local suppliers, and the best local suppliers amplified that advantage by getting close to customers in other ways. Suppliers knew their customers, knew what they wanted, and developed deep personal relationships to keep their customers' loyalty.

But those days are over. If we can associate the good, simple, local life with small town America, such as those in the heartland, we're not in Kansas anymore[3]. Yes, there are still small local businesses, but their proportion of the world's economy is declining. More importantly, their advantages have evaporated. A global Internet-based firm such as Amazon, or a global information-superior organization such as Marriott Hotels, can provide superior customer service to its customers, wherever they are. Customers want simplified interactions that give superior buying experiences, they want products and services that work at least as well as expected, and they want low prices. These critical elements of value are delivered best by companies that use information technology to remember their customers, offer them additional goods and services they will value, simplify their purchases, expedite delivery and installation, provide quick and effective service, and pass along cost savings resulting from efficient supply-chain management and volume purchasing discounts.

---

[3] For those too young to have seen it, these were Dorothy's words to her dog Toto when the tornado carried their house out of black-and-white Kansas into the Technicolor realm of Oz, in MGM's *The Wizard of Oz*.

The world has changed in so many ways over the last few years that the shape of things in the future has little in common with the stable features of the past. In this chapter we are going to discuss many of the big changes that, collectively, radically alter the environment for organizations and people. Taken together, these changes transport us from Kansas to a brave new world, where things never stop, information flows at light speed, the rich get richer, and new forms of intelligent life have the opportunity to dominate.

Networked World

We live in a networked world. Networks allow people to communicate telephonically or digitally, using a wide variety of means. Email and instant messaging are the most common forms of people-to-people digital communication. People also interact asynchronously by sharing files. New forms of digital communication include video teleconferencing and web-hosted conferences (or *webinars*). As communication costs decline, people communicate, collaborate, and cooperate more, because this enables them to make things happen more quickly, more effectively, and across greater distances.

Our machines have many ways to talk to one another as well. The Internet provides a ubiquitous basis for them to exchange messages and files. They can request services of one another or allow others to access their services and accomplish work remotely. They share databases, and these are often distributed among sub-databases and replicated to assure high availability in multiple locations. Other network protocols also exist for allowing our machines to interact. The most prevalent protocols operate on both "wired" networks and wireless ones.

In a matter of just a few years, there will be more devices communicating with one another on Earth than there are people. Why is this? Miniaturization enables us to build incredibly cheap sensors, computers, and transmitters. These provide useful information about the state of affairs in their local environment. Collecting this information enables organizations to track and update their models of the world, thereby giving them better information sooner. Most interesting machines in the future will link themselves up with some global network such as the Internet and immediately begin providing real-time data and receiving tasking orders from their masters.

What do machines say to each other when they talk? The history of information systems shows a steady progression in content from very simple status signals to higher levels of requests, transactions, and semantics. The

Internet solved the problem of allowing any computer to join the community of machines that can easily exchange digital information. The next problem solved was what the format and encoding of information should be. The Internet defines a variety of MIME types that allow different forms of content to be exchanged[4]. Distributed computing standards such as OMG's CORBA[5] and W3C's Web Services[6] made it easy for one computer to directly control another or obtain services from it, regardless of where it is. Finally, computers have begun to understand the content of information. They receive helpful hints coded using syntactic and semantic markup techniques, including XML and related domain descriptions given in XML-encoded DTDs[7]. Soon, XML-extending techniques such as the DARPA-W3C semantic markup language OWL[8] will begin providing machines easily processed semantic information. These technologies allow people to annotate computerized messages to say what types of components they encode and what standard categories they employ. Furthermore, machines using parsing, language understanding, and inference techniques can interpret what the content asserts, what it means, and what actions to take in response. While far from perfect, these techniques are already widely used and getting better all the time.

In short, the world we live in has practically no boundaries that limit who can talk to whom, what can talk to what, what can be said, or who and what can understand and act on information. Once your purchase computers and pay for the electricity to operate them, it costs you nothing extra to accommodate incremental requests for communication. Thus, the marginal cost of communication has become essentially zero. In such a world, talk may be cheap, but it's increasingly ubiquitous, continuous, and material.

---

[4] The Internet Engineering Task Force (IETF) sets Internet standards. See www.ietf.org.

[5] The Object Management Group (OMG) develops standards for distributed computing. See www.omg.org.

[6] The World Wide Web Consortium (W3C) develops standards for HTML, XML, web services, and other web protocols. See www.w3c.org.

[7] A Domain Type Definitions (DTD) specifies the attributes and possible values that practitioners in a specific community should employ to annotate their contents. For example, the Dublin Core dictates how to describe library resources.

[8] The W3C OWL Web Ontology Language effort has recommended a standard. See www.w3.org/TR/owl-features.

Globalization

In Thomas Friedman's book, *The Lexus and the Olive Tree,* the New York Times correspondent described the pressures on countries to participate in globalization as "the golden straightjacket."[2] The potential rewards for joining the global community were so great, they presented opportunities for "gold" and other fortunes to the participants. According to conventional economic theory, each player in the global marketplace could leverage its special advantages to optimize its economic results. China, for example, could exploit low labor costs and high quality workmanship to excel at manufacturing. But know-how and capital would only consider moving to countries that provided them safety. To feel safe they need financial transparency. They also want assurances that thieves won't loot their assets, and this requires a moderate level of sociopolitical maturity. Corrupt and autocratic regimes would chafe under these requirements for open and fair systems. These new rules would feel like a straightjacket on their behavior. Put on this golden straightjacket, make money. Abuse or reject it, and watch know-how and capital flee.

Globalization is a major economic and political trend, aided by international institutions such as the World Trade Organization, GATT, the European Community, and NAFTA. Each of these organizations provides a framework for increasing international trade and dependency, often at the expense of some national sovereignty and autonomy. The companies that participate in this trade act as what Koestler called holons. Each company becomes a component of bigger transnational systems with goals and constraints of their own. At the same time, each company operates as a self-contained entity pursuing its own goals and directing its components and constituents on how best to play along.

Many large companies have built their own multi-national systems to operate effectively across national boundaries, within the constraints of international laws and treaties. In addition, collections of allied and affiliated companies have worked out arrangements to provide mutual aid and support to members of their commercial federations. In Japan, these are called *kereitsu*. In Korea, they are called *chaebol*. These Asian federations of allied companies coordinate their products, their plans, their distribution networks, and their financial systems to out-perform the competing federations. In other countries, dominant manufacturing or retailing companies simply call their own coordinated federations of companies *supply chains*. In the context of this book, of course, we see these as early and somewhat immature forms of hyper-beings.

Global integration is occurring now because communication costs have fallen dramatically, knowledge and information are mobile, and capital is plentiful. Countries have seen benefits to increasing trade and seek ways to increase employment opportunities for their citizens. Language and cultural barriers are ebbing, in part due to the spread of western, especially American, products and values.

Globalization is likely to continue, albeit it with fits and starts. Many people object to the loss of their local culture or the loss of independence. Others object to the "take-no-prisoners," "winner-take-all" attitude associated with rampant capitalism and its dominant players. Others object to the concentration of wealth that goes along with market dominance and to concentration of political power that typically accompanies it. Still others object to the loss of diversity associated with predominant products, raising concerns such as reduced innovation, increased vulnerability to disease or disruptions, and loss of local industries and economic base. All of these concerns have *prima facie* validity and are supported by plentiful evidence. Nevertheless, the rewards evidently have more motive power than the risks. Globalization moves inexorably forward.

Move Bits, not Molecules

Most of the economy of the world, at least through the 20th century, was tied to processes that extracted, refined, processed, and shipped physical materials and products. Since people need food, clothes, furnishings, tools and fuel, the importance of these activities isn't going away any time soon. On the other hand, the most rapid growth in the economy is in the information sector, where people consume bits not molecules. So it's bits that have the fastest growing value. We need to understand why this is and what it portends.

When Gutenberg invented movable type, it unleashed revolutionary changes throughout Europe. Surely it wasn't the type itself that had the impact, nor the symbols on the page, nor the pages printed, nor the weight and volume of the books shipped. None of these essentially physical qualities was more than accidentally associated with the revolution. It was, of course, "the word" that created the impact. That is, information was able to get to readers who were edified, informed, and inspired as a result of consuming it. If informing means telling someone something they don't know, the widespread dissemination of printed materials unleashed an informing torrent. For the first time, people could learn from others not in their immediate vicinity, experts could reach broad audiences, and everyday people could drink from a fountain of knowledge.

Digital communications, including computers, computer-readable media, the contents of the World Wide Web, and mass media are now spewing forth vastly more information than anyone can consume in a lifetime. The prolific results of scientists, engineers, researchers, and automated observation and analysis stations find their way both to printed pages and on-line digital repositories. Practically everything worth saying is stored digitally and accessible to nearly every person on Earth. Our stockpile of digital content is growing exponentially.

Two very important side effects of this trend have become evident. First, as the media conglomerates have learned, digital content is leaking from their controlled vaults. People get access to a few copies of a valued resource, and they replicate it and disseminate it broadly. This, of course, threatens the established royalty systems that have compensated authors and publishers for the last two centuries. Second, the value chains associated with selling and delivering products and services to customers are being significantly restructured. Customers value the end result they obtain from a purchase, but generally begrudge the time, effort, and expense they incur in actually purchasing the product or service. Furthermore, customers don't perceive their personal copies of standardized information as highly valuable, worthy of high costs. In fact, individuals can obtain most information for free, either from libraries, broadcast media, or file sharing.

As a consequence, two trends combine to squeeze sellers in an economic vise. First, sellers must use digital communications increasingly to give customers more of what they value and reduce the hassle and effort required. Second, customers perceive much of the information sellers provide them as a standardized, low-value commodity. For these reasons, new enterprises employ lean operations that move more bits and fewer molecules, delivering customers a higher ratio of perceived value at reduced cost. Company presence becomes more virtual, the activities more information-centric than physical, and interactions with customers move increasingly into cyberspace. Cyberspace is where we communicate and conduct transactions that require only bits to move. Of course, physical transactions will continue, but economic returns inexorably shift from physical operations to information processes.

Capital is Mobile

Capital is money people invest in businesses. Companies usually expend capital on things such as equipment or facilities, and supplies. Because businesses consume resources to create the things they offer for sale, they expend money to build up inventory and promote their products before they can actually sell them. Eventually, customers purchase the goods and services the company has offered, thereby agreeing to pay the company amounts termed *revenues*. Delays often occur between sales and the inflow of cash resulting from actual payments. The build up of inventory, the delays in cash, and other requirements for short-term expenses combine to make the company seek additional money, termed *working capital*. Thus, companies basically need capital for two reasons, furnishing and operating their business processes.

Capital comes from people who think they can earn a good profit by lending the company money or by purchasing ownership shares in the company. The people who provide capital are termed *investors*. In exchange for providing the money, investors hope to earn interest on loans, dividends on stock shares, or capital gains on stock ultimately sold at prices higher than originally paid.

At several times in history, capital has been scarce. Scarcity results either from investors having no money available or being unwilling to risk it in businesses. Investors generally behave en masse, since every investor lives in the same environment and experiences mostly the same conditions[3]. When several investors find conditions favorable to invest, most investors do. When several investors have a great deal of liquid assets standing at the ready for investment, most investors are also keeping significant assets in liquid form. As a result, aggregate investment waxes and wanes cyclically. With respect to the publicly traded firms whose stock shares trade on stock exchanges, the basic swings are called "bull" and "bear" markets. When people have cash and want to invest, the "bulls" are running. Money flows into companies and their stocks. At other times, as in the period between the end of 2000 and early 2003, the reverse occurs. The "bears" sell their stocks, hold onto their cash, and do not invest.

It used to be difficult for investors to place investments far from home, because they couldn't get good information about the prospective investment and they couldn't easily participate in an investment transaction. Those days are long gone. Money flows around the globe, enabled by global investment banking operations, mutual fund companies, and electronic trading networks. People, institutions, and transactions operate at great distances, at the speed of light, with money moving as a result of electronic transactions that in actuality only change bits in the account records of credits and debits.

There have been times when the total amount of cash available was scarce, because people wanted to hoard it, governments gobbled it up for wars or other nationalistic pursuits, or people reacted to governmental corruption or financial mismanagement by losing confidence in money. Fortunately, we have mostly avoided those problems for the last 50 years.

The net result, and the important one for this section, is that money is plentiful and moves easily. Today, capital is mobile. It moves to where the opportunities are. It doesn't stop at regional, national, or international boundaries. It flows to different regions of the world as the climate changes. There's more money than good investment opportunities. Much of the developed world is sitting on piles of cash that are earning less than 1% per year. These are historically low returns. Almost any good investment opportunity can attract significant capital. Thus, capital has become a relatively weak player, owing to the relative excess of supply compared to demand. This factor amplifies the relative power of distributed intelligent organizations. People with capital, investors, have much reduced influence, and distributed organizations can obtain capital in multiple locales.

Labor is Mobile and Work is Outsourced

The other traditional source of power has been labor. In fact, labor and capital often wrestled over their share of influence, power and control. Organized labor might be cheering the declining power of capital but for one fact: the power of labor has suffered a similar decline. The biggest single factor degrading labor's power is the ability of businesses to transfer operations to low-cost communities. Even if the business as a whole doesn't move its signs, places of sale, and headquarters, it can effectively move most of the value-adding work. So China has become the number one manufacturer in the world. Most American companies continue to transfer core manufacturing operations to China and other developing countries with low wages, such as Mexico, Vietnam and India. So businesses today can transfer work to components that pay workers low wages. This practice is termed *outsourcing*, and it is one of the single fastest growing trends in industry. Traditional blue-collar manufacturing has been moving for decades. White-collar outsourcing has moved in lock-step with the rise of modern networking and improved information processing capabilities.

Labor itself is increasingly capable of moving to where the work is. Europe is suffering from historically low birth rates, so workers from Turkey and underdeveloped countries of the former Soviet Union travel to take up places in Western European businesses. For decades, Latin Americans have flooded the US to perform vital jobs in agriculture and service industries that kept wages in these occupations below American citizens' official "poverty" levels.

Both means of getting work done at lower labor rates have been accelerating. It's relatively easy in today's world to ship bits to a low-wage locale describing the products and processes that machines and workers need to implement. Even customers who telephone the toll-free service number for their best known national companies are likely to be speaking to people half a world away, all made possible by modern telecommunications and computing. The individual workers in the low-wage locale can be local residents or can get there in a few hours by catching a low-cost airplane flight. Labor, on a global scale, is vastly underutilized. There are many more potential workers than high paying jobs. Supply, again, exceeds demand. Our networks and open borders make labor mobile and put it under great competitive pressure.

A recent news[9] report extolling significantly improved business results achieved by Cisco after the e-commerce bubble burst, makes the point clearly:

> [Cisco management] began playing hardball with suppliers to keep profits up. The CEO of one supplier said Cisco wanted to take 90 days to pay for his products instead of the normal 30. It also wanted the supplier to extend the warranty on its goods to three years from one. When he balked, the CEO got a call from a midlevel manager. "If you don't [agree to our terms], we'll instruct our people not to use your products," he recalls the manager saying. The supplier, like many others in such tough times, couldn't afford to lose Cisco's business and buckled under.
>
> Many others lost out entirely. Cisco's list of key suppliers has fallen from 1,300 to 420. That lowered administrative

---

[9] *Business Week,* November 24, 2003.

costs and led to volume discounts worth hundreds of millions of dollars each year. Pond also outsourced more production to lower costs, from 45% in 2000 to over 90% today. At the same time, he spent millions to shift production work from nine contract manufacturers to just four. And smaller resellers complain that Cisco began giving discounts to strategic distribution partners such as IBM and SBC Communications, leaving hundreds of smaller players unable to compete against these behemoths. "Cisco went from being our best partner in good times to our worst enemy in bad times," says the former CEO of one reseller.

The end result is that the deck is stacked to make it easy for businesses to cut costs continually by moving work to the lowest cost workers. The better organized, the more globally conscious, the more intelligent the distributed operations, the lower the costs, the higher the profits, the greater the natural size and scale of the prevailing enterprises. Conditions are very conducive to the rise of hyper-beings.

Excessive Supply

Michael Hammer, in his book *Agenda,* tried to rally company executives to change their perception from business as usual[4]. He pointed out that we, in the developed world, live in environments of plenty. In fact, there are *too many* suppliers of almost everything. Most customers don't perceive significant differences among the products offered by competing companies. Moreover, even the CEOs of most companies admit in private discussions that *they* don't perceive significant differences either. When products are indistinguishable, they are by definition *commodities*. When we have more commodities on the market than customers with money really want, we've got a situation of excess supply. That is the world we occupy.

Hammer's point was that old strategies don't work for companies in this situation. You can operate your business, if you're extremely efficient, but you will net minimal profits, if any. To get big profits from customers, you must offer them something they see as different and worth a premium price. The simplest road to profitability is through this kind of differentiation. But if you cannot differentiate your products, you have to differentiate around the customer's experience. What do most customers want? Better, faster, cheaper products, services, and results, with minimum hassle. When everybody's making the same things, nobody can differentiate by making better, faster, or cheaper products. Advantages of that sort are short-lived and usually insignificant. Unless you invent new types of products, improving the customer's experience may be your only profitable gambit. How do you give a customer a superior experience? You need to: know the customer better; simplify the customer's buying experiences; reduce customer hassles associated with delivery, installation, support and maintenance; and win the customer's continuing loyalty through periodic positive interactions. This is the *agenda* for surviving, thriving, and making profits in commoditized markets with excessive supply.

When products were simple, distance a big obstacle, and customers naïve, every small business serving its local clientele could address this full agenda with a warm, friendly, ongoing relationship. Today's products, however, often have greater complexity, and customers have become increasingly sophisticated. If assistance is required, it cannot be provided by technically ignorant, general-purpose sales personnel or call center attendants. When a customer wants help, not hassle, the company has to link the customer directly to a knowledgeable specialist. That specialist, to be really effective, should know the customer's history, have a model of the customer's product and site configuration, and have unsurpassed knowledge of how to make things work when problems arise. As products increasingly interact on networks with other products and combine software components from multiple sources, the challenge of providing excellent service seems beyond the ken of any company. Moreover the outsourcing trend means that most customers are being supported by low-paid, uninformed, unfamiliar personnel, leaving the customer with the unpleasant experience of having incurred additional injury as a result of seeking assistance.

To reduce a customer's hassle and to exceed the customer's expectation for a positive interaction, companies literally will need to provide super-human service to customers. Their service will remember each customer perfectly, know the customer's history totally, be familiar with the customer's configuration and site, know how these components interact, understand a wide range of service objectives and problems, be capable of diagnosing and repairing problems remotely, and be thoughtful enough to offer the customer additional benefits, savings, promotions, and innovations that the customer considers outstanding. Without these capabilities, all companies, regardless of size, will slip into mediocrity and eventual demise. Only large companies with comprehensive technical capabilities can accomplish this agenda. They will do this by superior use of information about customers, products, configurations, sites, problems, diagnoses, objectives, opportunities, and support techniques. They will use built-in sensing, networked communication, surveillance and management techniques to reach into customers' premises, watch what's going on, and proactively deliver superior customer experiences. The companies that do this will grow into dominant hyper-beings in the competitive arena. Their customers will be wowed, delighted, and loyal.

Power to the Buyer

Ironically, in a world of giant companies, power is shifting to the buyer. When many companies offer equivalent commodities, the customer can freely choose among suppliers. The suppliers will bid to win the customer's business, and they will inevitably compete by offering lower prices or enhanced packages. Almost every industry today is awash in competitive blood-letting, where prices are falling and companies are starving for customers. Current examples are evident in PCs, computer servers, telephones and wireless services, banking, insurance, jeans, groceries, airlines, hotels, and rental cars. As more services come on line to help customers break through remaining barriers to price information, prices will inevitably fall further. Thus, the Internet accelerates the decline of profits among commodity suppliers.

Sellers have traditionally used many different techniques to lock their customers into their product line and keep them from switching to other suppliers. There have been proprietary operating systems, proprietary hardware, proprietary networks, proprietary adapters, proprietary order entry systems, proprietary distribution and delivery networks, proprietary telephone numbers, proprietary instant messaging systems, etc. All of these were intended mostly to cause the user great difficulty and expense for switching suppliers. These systems are supposed to be very "sticky," being somewhere between "honey" and "fly-paper." Attractive properties are excellent, because they bring in new customers. Lock-in features are excellent, because they prevent existing customers from departing.

Consumer groups and governments often work to break down the lock-in features of proprietary products. Standards, in particular, are used to define how multiple competitors in a market should make their products work together. This increases the "openness" of the market and reduces proprietary lock-in. When all the suppliers in a market offer products that compete and interoperate, customers have maximum power. When a single dominant supplier controls the market, that defines a monopoly. Governments eventually attack monopolies, finding ways to open the market and increase customer power. Monopolists derive big profits, but eventually governments reduce them.

In our current environment, characterized by a surfeit of undifferentiated products, the customer has more power than the supplier. Customers are getting smarter too, because they have access to more and better information that reveals features, prices, and competitive comparisons. In this world, customers won't pay premium prices to any supplier that provides merely competitive features and prices. There isn't much wiggle room for the mediocre business.

Innovate or Die

Many middle-class and affluent adults have begun to experience the combined effects of globalization, outsourcing, and surplus supply: they're losing their jobs, their total compensation doesn't keep up with the rising costs of a comfortable life, and they have become and feel dispensable. Whole sectors of the economy and even whole nations risk falling down the ladder of economic progress. In bygone days, with protected markets and other barriers to friction-free flow of information, capital, and workers, industrial giants and their governmental allies could maintain supremacy. Now, however, no giant protects its workers in one country from lower-priced workers in another country. No legislature can build a barrier to stop the flows. Operating according to yesterday's strategies won't arrest the slide.

Joseph Schumpeter was the first economist to explain how innovation works to expand the economy and why we need as much of it as we can get to sustain rising standards of living [5-7]. Most modern businesses realize that they must continually create and nurture new products and services. As sales of these new offerings increase, they offset revenue reductions resulting from formerly significant but increasingly stale products. Our employers can afford to achieve innovation and increase productivity by moving jobs to low-cost labor forces. This becomes easy once these labor forces raise their education and innovation skills to levels comparable to those in North America, Europe and Japan. But we, as individuals, can't afford to have them take away and transfer our employment, and we as a nation can't afford to have the national economic advantages deteriorate. No matter what level of analysis you consider—the individual, the company, or the nation—the logic is simple: *innovate or die!* Declines are slow, so even severe disorders might not be obvious, and death isn't immediate. But sliding down the ladder of prosperity hurts enormously.

The message is clear. As individuals, we need to excel at innovative thinking and processes. As suppliers and employees, we need to participate in organizations that out-perform the competition, continually, including over the long-haul. As citizens, we need to assure that political, social, economic and educational policies sustain our advantages in innovation. A few leading CEOs, all of whom lead efforts to shift large amounts of capital, employment, and opportunity out of the US, are at least trying to raise the alarm before more "canaries in the mine" die. The following news item illustrates their alarm:

"OCTOBER 30, 2003 (REUTERS) - IBM CEO Samuel Palmisano said today that the U.S. needs to step up the pace of innovation to help stem the flow of technology jobs overseas.

Palmisano said that he expects 13 million jobs to be created in the next two years around the world, including in rapidly developing countries such as China, India and South Korea.

"We are at a critical moment," he said. "Because if we're not careful, the U.S. will fall out of step with the new realities of innovation. If that were to happen, the innovators and risk-takers would go elsewhere. Because today they can."

Palmisano spoke at the annual meeting of the Council on Competitiveness in Washington, which is creating a National Innovation Initiative to come up with ideas on how to continue to innovate in the face of such competition.

Other countries are becoming more competitive not only in wages but also in education, job skills and network infrastructure, he said. "We believe the United States must again raise the bar — to take the steps necessary to keep the nation at the forefront, to continue to offer the most fertile and attractive environment for innovation in the world."

His comments come at a time when IBM and other companies are shifting jobs overseas as they try to cut costs.

Last week, Intel Corp. CEO Craig Barrett said that the semiconductor company no longer planned to invest in California and that its investments were following its markets, 70% of which are outside the U.S.

Earlier this month, Intel Corp. co-founder Andrew Grove said that U.S. dominance in key tech sectors was at risk, comparing it to the fate of the U.S. steel industry. "It would be a miracle if it didn't happen in the software and services industry," Grove said.

The comments also come about six months after the head of Oracle Corp., technology industry veteran Larry Ellison, stirred up controversy by saying that innovation was all but gone in the U.S. and that Silicon Valley, the home of start-up technology companies, was dead."

Knowledge is Power

Knowledge is information about how the world works. With knowledge, we can anticipate how one thing affects another, we can predict effects, and we can often control what does or does not occur. Knowledge derives mostly from *science*, where investigators formulate hypotheses, run experiments, and hone theories and explanations that work reliably. People have a great deal of *informal* knowledge, as well, gained as a result of their brains doing pseudo-scientific analyses of their personal experiences. When many people have compatible experiences and interpretations, their informal knowledge becomes generally accepted. Scientific knowledge explains how antibiotics work, how engines produce thrust, how bridges stand and airplanes fly, and how electronics carry information over networks that display messages. Informal knowledge explains why insults engender anger, faithfulness produces trust, speeding causes stress, and why it's better to seek forgiveness than permission. Regardless of what type of knowledge we possess, knowledge that's valid enables us to predict and control events in the world. That is why *knowledge is power.*

When engineers speak of *power* they mean the capability to accomplish physical work in some reasonable amount of time. The more power, the faster you can move a heavy weight or the more weight you can throw around. This is a different but analogous meaning of that intended when we speak of the *power* of knowledge. In the current case, we mean that knowledge can enable you to do all kinds of work in improved ways. If you want to move more weight, knowledge can enable you to do that. If you want to move a weighty object faster, knowledge can enable you. If you want to do things better, or faster, or cheaper, the most direct route is through know-how. In short, knowledge amplifies physical power.

From the fossil and archaeological record, we have good evidence that most of human history was marked by an incredibly negligible growth of knowledge. Even in historical times, whole centuries passed with few advances in knowledge. That changed a few hundred years ago starting with the Renaissance, and knowledge has been increasing since then at an accelerating rate

Many of our new technologies directly support the knowledge-producing industries and processes. Recently, for example, the entire human genome was sequenced by robots. Machines implemented the techniques of trained microbiologists, computers processed the data to identify valid hypotheses, and other computer programs automatically documented the results. The same kind of acceleration is happening in most areas of human endeavor. Even when processes are not fully automated, scientists and researchers collaborate via networks, publish their results on Internet-accessible databases or web sites, search for others' relevant results, and analyze and interpret results using powerful networks of computers with sophisticated data processing algorithms. Computers can conjecture hypotheses, design and conduct experiments, analyze and publish results. The whole process of finding truth now operates at light speed.

Through automation and productivity enhancements for human investigators, civilization is producing knowledge at a breakneck pace. In addition, observations and reports are spewing forth from automated collectors, pundits, bloggers, journalists, critics, students, teachers, and columnists. All of this information is digitally encoded, widely indexed, and instantly available. This is a "good news, bad news" situation. On the plus side, we have more information and more knowledge about what it means than we can reasonably hope to exploit. On the negative side, the average individual is awash in digital data and has no hope of finding, let alone benefiting from, more than a tiny fraction of what's available. The game is definitely tilting in favor of teams of people over the individual, especially hyper-beings and other information-superior organizations that have the resources, processes, and incentives to find the best information, exploit it, and surpass their competition.

Because knowledge is accumulating rapidly, new possibilities open. New understanding of how things work makes it possible to invent new products and processes, as well as to improve existing products and processes through more limited innovations. In computing and electronics, we have been watching product life-cycles shrink for some time. Most products are succeeded by new versions in about a year, and significant new families of products arise about every 5 to 10 years now. These cycles are about twice as fast as they were 20 years ago and about 10 times faster than they were 100 years ago. The more we learn, the greater the opportunity to change what we offer the customer, to jump ahead of the pack, to extract more money by giving noticeably more value for the same price.

In competitive arenas other than business, knowledge is equally powerful. In intellectual arenas, such as chess, knowledge and the ability to apply it quickly have long been determinative. Only in the last few years have the know-how and proficiency of computers reached the level of the world's best human chess players. In medicine, as another example, computers routinely analyze and interpret medical data, guide surgical interventions, monitor and manage patients.

In military contests, the information-superior organization is able to prevent conflict, shape the battlefield when conflict is inevitable, and win decisively by outthinking and outmaneuvering the opponent. The information-superior organization collects more useful information, interprets it more correctly, exploits it for better plans, and distributes information more usefully, in a more timely way, to enable its distributed components to coordinate their activities more effectively. The end result is that the modern military aspires to harness and leverage the power a hyper-being's superior knowledge provides.

In sum, the production of information is up throughout the world, it moves faster than before, and knowledge about how things work and how to exploit information is increasing exponentially. Knowledge makes innovation and invention possible, and these are the easiest routes to profit. Knowledge of the customer, the customer's business, and the customer's problems provides the means for a business to deliver value, to differentiate its offerings, and to charge premium prices customers gladly pay. In military and non-profit spheres, success also comes to the smart organization that can get better information and employ it effectively across boundaries. Size and reach multiply the power of knowledge, because they create more opportunities to employ it for advantage. Hyper-beings, organizations of great size and reach, possessing superior information processing systems, are uniquely equipped to transform the knowledge explosion into a competitive advantage.

24x7 **Competition**

What ever happened to "bankers' hours?" Ah, it must have been nice: working weekdays only 9 am to 3 pm, possibly as late as 6 pm on Fridays. Nice job, if you can get it, eh? Well, as you know, those jobs are gone, along with the slow pace of competition they reflected. Competition today is 24 x 7: 24 hours per day, seven days per week, 365 days per year. Why? Because customers have the power, labor is cheap relative to the fixed costs of big businesses, the information processing infrastructure runs all the time without marginal costs incurred by the hour, and buyers buy more when free to shop on their own timetables. One other factor is increasingly important in this shift, and that is the rise of *virtual stores* or *e-business*. Shoppers no longer care where the sellers are located. Online, they shop when they want and where they want. Many sellers are represented mostly or entirely by computers that present shopping pages and forms, accept purchase orders, and complete the transactions entirely electronically. Ultimately, goods may be transshipped from the manufacturer or distributor directly to the customer, with no molecules ever passing through the hands of the seller.

Only cultural and legal barriers might slow proliferation of the 7x24 model. "Blue laws" used to prevent people from selling alcoholic beverages on Sundays and election days. Similar laws used to prevent retailers from selling on Sundays and other unwholesome times. And in many countries, various restrictions still impede big business invasion of local markets. These constraints, though still in place in some jurisdictions, are vanishing fast. Globalization brings with it requirements for open markets. Foreign companies bring with them desires to serve the customer at all hours of the day, at all places around the globe. In this arena, the sun never sets, for the enterprise is serving customers around the clock and around the globe.

Obviously organizations that work around the clock must be supported by information systems that never sleep. Financial transactions keep coming, order processing goes on continuously, and goods and services are being delivered somewhere every instant. The ability to integrate the far-flung operations of a global enterprise 24 hours a day is a stunning achievement of computer and communications technology augmented by powerful software applications. Organizations that employ this technology effectively and efficiently gain huge advantages. Once in place, organizations can use this technological foundation as a basis for observing, monitoring, coordinating, and managing the entire operations. These organizations attain information superiority by joining its extensive information to its comprehensive abilities to plan, execute, and control. Operating non-stop with the best systems and the best information sets a pace that few competitors can match.

Asymmetries and Asymmetric Threats

Information superiority has natural economies of scale. The networks, processes, products and behaviors get better, faster and cheaper the more people they serve. In traditional "smoke stack" industries, natural economies of scale occur too, but they usually lead to monopolies that require government regulation. Electric power and telephone were two industries that, for most of their histories, were regulated because of such economies of scale. There is some debate about whether they should have ever been deregulated, but political deals broke these industries into multiple parts under the belief that innovation would increase and consumers would reap benefits from increased competition. Until these recent experiments however, conventional economic wisdom about these industries held that the average cost of serving customers would decrease as the companies expanded. Thus, once a company got ahead, it could progress steadily toward complete monopoly by exploiting its cost advantages to undercut any competitor.

The reason for this discussion is to make the point that *big is better in networks*. The more links, nodes, and users you have, the more customers you can serve and the lower your average costs. If your networks provide some other advantage, such as knowledge or improved decision making, the benefits of scale increase. Big isn't just better in that case, *big is everything*. An organization that has greater reach, more information, more knowledge, and more intelligent processes needs only capital and labor to fuel its dominant position. It can crush competitors with superior products, services, customer knowledge, and costs. Being Number 1 isn't everything. It's the only thing.

I have intentionally stressed the objective advantages of the dominant hyper-beings to drive up your desire to look for weaknesses in the argument. If you are like me, you find one-sided contests and one-sided arguments offensive. Although you and I are engaged here in a purely intellectual exchange, the organizations that are facing competition from hyper-beings experience the reality of this argument as a daily threat to their existence. It's not a game for them. To operate in a niche where an information-superior hyper-being lives is to look Death in the face. Death in business may mean closing down an operation and the loss of jobs for people who presently earn a living wage. In military contests, however, death means death.

Over the last few years, the asymmetric nature of military competition with the United States has been a topic of intense investigation in the US, among our allies, among other nation states, and among terrorists. It doesn't take long for people to realize that the dumbest thing you can do is to attack or oppose a superior power in ways that let it exploit its superiority against you. Instead, you look for ways to attack it that play to its weaknesses or which nullify the power of its many advantages. This gives rise to asymmetric threats and asymmetric warfare.

The 9/11 terrorist acts illustrate this asymmetry. The terrorists used the US's own commercial assets to attack a non-military target of great symbolic significance. The total destruction of the World Trade Center was emotionally devastating. The suicide of the attackers negated our ability to retaliate or wreak vengeance. This created a sense of powerlessness. Finally, the stateless nature of the Al-Qaeda meant we had nothing we could attack in retaliation. Although we have subsequently toppled governments in Afghanistan and Iraq ostensibly in some way to respond to the 9/11 attack, most people can see how tenuous and strained this logic is. In asymmetric warfare, the smaller opponent doesn't play by your rules. It minimizes or negates your power by nullifying your logic. It seeks ways to have huge negative impacts on the general public rather than military or state targets.

The US and the rest of the developed world have great advantages that are driving the rise and growth of hyper-beings, but we also have sensitive dependencies on vulnerable supporting systems. We cannot make these systems totally secure, and taxpayers consider the costs prohibitive to make these even moderately safe. Food, water, highways, airports, trains, telephones, electric power grids, the Internet, Microsoft PCs, Linux servers, financial networks, credit cards, drivers' licenses, employee databases, social security numbers, etc., etc., are all vulnerable and relatively easy for talented people to attack. We have a society and industrial base that thrived in an environment of low external threat and widespread domestic tranquility. When we built systems for defense, we oriented them toward great military attacks from the East. By the time the Soviet Union collapsed, the defense establishments on both sides of the Atlantic were basically bankrupt.

We do not have now, nor are we likely to have soon, effective means of preventing or countering a wide range of asymmetric threats. In the national security arena, this means we will be scrambling to improve our abilities to detect, prevent, and mitigate a huge diversity of possible attacks on largely undefended targets. The opponents of America's hegemony correctly see the hyper-beings that spring from our culture as sprawling dominant organizations. They also understand that these hyper-beings will prevail in peaceful environments governed by familiar rules and values. Their only means of attacking that hegemony is through asymmetries. We should expect a great number of these in the future.

Similarly, in contexts other than military, we should expect a large number of asymmetric challenges to the hegemony of hyper-beings. People and organizations that see their livelihoods challenged and see all advantages going to the other side will do desperate things.

Can anything be done to prevent these nasty scenarios from playing out? Assuming that the hyper-beings will dominate in civilized competitive arenas, we must ask how much inequality between winners and losers will be tolerated. Presumably, by sharing the wealth, winners can create a world of tolerable disparity. That, however, requires a degree of self-serving enlightenment and government involvement that has been rare in human history. We can only hope that the inevitable predominance of hyper-beings is not allowed to run to its natural, monopolistic, asymmetric end. Powerful interests need powerful limiters.

Summary

Much of natural evolution has led to the predominance of the human (*homo sapiens*), the thinking and talking creature who uses tools, reasons symbolically, models the world, and predicts and controls processes to achieve desired outcomes. In the 20th century, engineers created tools and technologies that allow large organizations of people, and collections of organizations, and collections of organizations and computers to combine forces to control more things, more effectively. These emerging hyper-beings know how to get desired results. They can assess their situation, set goals, develop credible plans, anticipate results their plans will produce, implement plans, control execution, observe outcomes, learn from experience, innovate and continually improve. In aggregate, these activities define what I call *efficient thought*. Hyper-beings think more efficiently because they have more and better resources, more knowledge and better information, and better processes.

Hyper-beings extend evolution beyond individuals, beyond organizations, into a new class of distributed, intelligent, multi-level, bio-electronic hybrid life forms. Where in the past advantages might have accrued purely to size, strength, wealth, or physical skills, the quality of an organization's thinking most determines success in the future. What matters most is the organization's ability to achieve good outcomes in a dynamic environment by correctly understanding how things work, having the ability to formulate, evaluate, and implement good plans, and executing plans faster than agile competitors. All of these capabilities combine to make up efficient thought. The next chapter looks into these key capabilities more deeply.

3. Efficient Thought

Efficiency is the ability to produce desired effects with a minimum of effort and waste. *Thought* is the product of reasoning. When we combine these two, we have the essence of the competitive advantage of humans over other animals, of smart people over dull ones, of great companies over mediocre ones. As information processing capabilities have increased and improved, through the revolutionary progress in computing and telecommunications, they have multiplied the competitive advantages arising from the superior intellect of the efficient thinkers. Understanding efficient thought is vitally important for two reasons. First, in the competitive environment, it's vital that you understand how you compare with your competitors on important factors. Second, this is a factor that we can directly affect; we can improve the efficiency of our thought almost without limit. Those that focus on improving their thinking efficiency will magnify their advantages. Those that don't will surely fall behind desperately.

There's a familiar aphorism that hits very close to the essential truth: *Working smarter beats working harder.* This old saw captures out culture's understanding of the idea that choosing the smartest thing to do at each point in time leads to much better outcomes than those we get by merely increasing the intensity of formerly successful activities. The people who live by this creed usually reveal a teeny bit of smugness, as if being unable to suppress an ebullient sense of superiority. This feeling emanates from a feeling that they don't have to work as many hours, they don't have to exert themselves as hard, and they get better results than their competitors get. All of these they believe come from the fact that they put their energy into better plans, based on better ideas, than the competition does. While there can be many spurious or accidental reasons for an individual's personal success, there's no doubt that the better informed, more thoughtful, quicker reacting players collectively and on average get much better results. In competition between species, groups, or organizations, those odds are enough in the long run to lead to total domination of the information-superior competitors.

In later chapters, we'll delve somewhat deeply into some technologies for efficient thought and intelligent systems. For the moment, though, let's consider some of the more macroscopic elements of efficient thought. Specifically, let's identify some of the biggest ideas that enable information-superior creatures to think winning thoughts. In doing this, it helps to start with a brief overview of the nature of human superiority.

When we say that humans are superior to other animals, what do we mean? We surely don't mean in size, strength, speed or other physical qualities. There is, in fact, no identifiable physical property of humans that would rank them at the top of the heap in a physical competition. In contrast, we have gained enormous advantages through our ability to think, to plan, to obtain desired results. We have learned much about how the world works, primarily through science and experience-based learning. We have written down much of this knowledge and taught it to subsequent generations. As the world changes and we adapt, we modify our knowledge and pass along current best methods to the next generations. The generally shared knowledge constitutes the public culture, and this culture carries much of the retained earnings of our collective enterprise. In various private or otherwise restricted circles, we have smaller versions of these cultural practices. In long-lived companies and various governmental agencies, the humans actively employ current knowledge to seek superior results, refine it based on lessons learned, codify and teach it to new members. While we can easily see honeybees accumulating pollen and storing it as honey for the next generation, it takes some distance and vision to recognize that we humans are doing pretty much the same thing. But, as a result of being the information-superior beings, we aren't working on molecules of sugar. Instead, we are refining, storing, and transmitting bits of information. We have as many hives as organizations and cultures we actively participate in.

Does this metaphor reveal more than it obscures? Do we really spend our lives processing information? Are we really totally dependent for survival on out ability to think efficiently? While it may be difficult to see the situation up close, consider some comparisons over a slightly larger scale. Consider, for example, how Stone-Age people would fare in the modern world. The last remaining Stone-Age people on Earth need to be protected, as endangered species. They have no means of protecting themselves from competitive pressures that modern man would put on them. They have no weapons that threaten us. Their means of hunting and farming are so primitive that they would perish if their ecological resources were taken over by higher productivity economic entities. They'd be relegated to poor land with no practical value. Their education doesn't move the successive generations forward so, in comparison with other humans, they continue to fall further behind. They have no means of preventing disease, building new means of production, or creating and distributing innovations to earn a decent wage. The chasm between today's people with yesterday's thinking, from a competitive viewpoint, is unbridgeable. Yesterday's thinking is a lethal liability.

Humans use a small number of powerful techniques to achieve superiority over other animals and other human competitors. They innovate and experiment, trying new ways to get desirable results. They learn from successes, tending to repeat what previously appeared to produce good outcomes. They especially learn from failures. They often dwell for long periods asking themselves "Why?" bad things happened. A victim of failure will endlessly explore mental alternatives in "If only..." and "What if..." dialogues. The person carries on these dialogues occasionally with other real people and, even more often, with simulated parties contained entirely in his or her own head. Information-superior entities react quickly to failures and disasters, shifting rapidly from grief and humiliation to a new resolve to "get back up on the horse" and get back into the game. Assuming one makes a reasoned interpretation as to the cause of the failure and avoids that in the future, prospects for success increase. The faster one sets about confirming the new approach, the more competitive advantage accrues.

The more motivated one feels to understand the cause of failure and to discover a better way in the future, the more likely the entity is to improve its knowledge and its future outcomes. The more effective the reasoning, the more effective the experimentation and scientific method, and the more frugal the expenditures, the more predictably the learning competitor pulls ahead of others. The essence of human superiority boils down to the discipline of doing better in the future by improving one's understanding of the world and using that superior knowledge to formulate and implement plans that produce ever better outcomes. If we suffer emotional distress and humiliation as a result of past failures, we need to understand how evolution uses these to spur us to find alternative knowledge and behaviors that lead us away from these disappointments in the future.

Other capabilities, especially those related to human communication, play important roles in advancing human superiority over animals. These important capabilities enable us to communicate, share information, collaborate, and extract information from what others tell us. However, we are going to ignore them momentarily so we can focus on the primacy of efficient thought. Even if we did all those other things superbly, weak or inefficient thinking would diminish our prospects. Communication and information assets multiply advantages that efficient thought provide. Thus, efficient thought lies at the crux of our inquiry.

The next few sections describe the principal facets of efficient thought, providing a basic agenda for individuals and organizations that aspire to competitive dominance. The elements on this agenda define what we must do, as a minimum, in our personal behavior and our enterprise processes. I will lay out six points, each intended to be easily memorized. These half-dozen objectives define in an operational way what we must ask our information-processing systems, personnel, and processes to do for us. Later in the book, we'll introduce metrics for these behaviors that allow you to measure and continually improve your performance on these vital activities.

Knowledge is Power, Ignorance is <u>Not</u> Bliss

The person who first thought "ignorance is bliss" didn't have a competitive environment in mind. While an unawareness of problems can reduce dissatisfaction, it doesn't reduce threats from competitors. Wariness of predators is a prerequisite for survival. Thriving in a competitive world requires much more. At a minimum, we have to *know* how to get what we want and keep others from blocking our aspirations. The more we know, the more plans can we consider, the more alternatives can we implement, and the more tactics can we employ to thwart those who would block us. In cases where we must prevail over a competitor or defeat a mortal enemy, our very survival will depend on out-thinking them. For all these reasons, *knowledge is power.*

Rulers, chieftains, and popes have always appreciated the potency of knowledge. For these reasons, they employed scientists and scholars, as well as alchemists and spies. Collecting, assessing and interpreting information came to be known as *intelligence,* somewhat confusing two different things: (1) quality information; and (2) the advantageous exploitation of information to achieve superior outcomes. In any case, for as long as people and organizations have competed with one another for power and privilege, the hunt for know-how and people who could advance it was put at the top of the agenda.

The information age has amplified the importance of knowledge and the ability to employ it. Much of our economy reflects this importance. We train our elite for more than 20 years, and we continue to invest in increasing and refining their knowledge for decades. Each person in the modern economy must engage in continuous learning to take advantage of the new findings that our scientific and technological establishments spew forth. Few areas of human activity avoid the grinding pressures created by the torrent of new knowledge and new ways of making things work. Just keeping up with the average performer in an information-age economy requires every participant to learn more and more every year. In mortal competition, in business or on the battlefield, everything you know is an asset and everything you don't know is a weakness. *Knowing* means being able to do. *Not knowing* means merely hoping the other is more ignorant than you. Both in business and war, that's a terrifying prospect.

Dominant organizations understand that knowledge is the most powerful weapon in their arsenals. In short, *knowledge is power.*

Plan Ahead

The second important thing intelligent entities ought to understand is the imperative to *plan ahead.* When I speak of a *plan,* I mean a blueprint or design for future actions. Plans specify future actions schematically. A plan is rarely 100% detailed. We need to simplify complexity and reduce details so that we can reasonably quickly analyze and assess candidate plans. We might omit the exact time of an action, the name of a participant, the details of a tool, or the exact amount of expendable resources. In each plan, some factors predominate, and others are secondary or negligible.

Because the difficulty of thinking increases with the number of details, even powerful supercomputers normally must suppress many details to reason about plans. As you know from personal experience, assessing plans is challenging. Even when we are considering just a single candidate plan, it may take hours, days or weeks to judge the likely effects of a plan, the factors most important to its success, the aspects most vulnerable to external factors, and the expected implementation costs. To come up with a *good* plan may require considering a few or dozens of alternatives. Finding the best possible plan in an exponentially large search space may require brilliant insights into the very structure of that space. Short of finding the best plan, we may settle for seeking an excellent plan. In many arenas, this requires that we generate and evaluate millions of alternatives or more.

If evaluating one candidate plan takes a long time, finding an excellent one can take a very, very long time. Since the whole point of planning is to execute a cunning maneuver in the real world before we lose the contest to our competition, we probably shouldn't sit around cogitating for weeks, months or years before making our move. For these reasons, we'd better *plan ahead.*

Scientists in many fields study the nature of good plans, how people develop them, and how they execute them. We will discuss much of that in later chapters. For the moment, we want to convey the most important generalizations. As indicated above, plans vary in how much detail they include or exclude. They also vary in the time span they cover. In planning routes for aircraft, for example, the air traffic control system initially looks out in time for as long as the intended flight will last, usually several hours. In actually adjusting the on-going flights of en route aircraft, planners look ahead tens of minutes to assure that all aircraft will remain safely separated while moving expeditiously toward their destinations. Such planning is redone, repetitively, every few minutes to re-assess, re-adjust, and re-validate that all aircraft will achieve good outcomes.

So how many things are considered, how far into the future we look, and how often we re-plan varies from one field of endeavor to another. Plans for military deployments and battlefield campaigns are among the most complex, most detailed, and most frequently re-planned. Most businesses, by contrast, develop strategic plans on a multi-year periodic basis, and these plans are usually very abstract, lacking in detail, and rarely adjusted. Regardless of the scope, detail, and frequency of revisiting, plans take considerable time to create, assess, and select, and they control our behavior for considerable lengths of time once implemented. If "timeliness is next to godliness," planning in advance is what enables us to get there on time, ready to go.

Throw the Plan Out

Military commanders are fond of tweaking the planning community by attesting that the first thing a commander does when conflict breaks out is to "throw the plan out." The kernel of truth in this assertion is that whatever plan we may have prepared in advance must have incorporated a large number of assumptions about the state of the world, the intentions of our enemies, the capabilities of our coalition partners, and so forth. These assumptions were required to provide enough detail to determine how many resources would be required, where they would be positioned, and what their objectives and responsibilities would be. Inevitably, reality invalidates some of these assumptions. The choice of plan and its evaluation may now rest upon an invalidated justification. There's nothing left to do but re-plan. As soon as a new and better plan can be identified and implemented, we want to throw out the original plan and replace it with the new one.

The new plan, unfortunately, suffers from the same flaw almost the moment we begin to implement it, because the world and its actors don't behave exactly the way we thought they would. In fact, even our own team members don't do exactly what we ask them to or accomplish precisely what we thought they would. In many ways, the world seems to want to disappoint, discourage, and thwart us. Our competitors strive to do this intentionally. Everyone else just seems to have a knack for it.

The important point here is that, while no plan can ever perfectly anticipate the state of affairs when it begins to execute or how the world will change as the plan executes, operating according to excellent plans produces the best possible results. We must plan as well as possible so that we can produce the most predictable positive outcomes. At the same time, we must continually try to get better information and better knowledge. We must exploit these findings rapidly to create revised plans that be put into execution promptly. Thus, superior organizations focus on improving intelligence, planning and control, as well as continuous monitoring, assessment, critique, learning, and re-planning, Much as writers learn the success formula, "writing is rewriting," information-superior organizations know the corresponding success formula for competitive dynamic arenas: "planning is re-planning."

Get Murphy before He Gets You

Engineers are very familiar with Murphy's Law, which states, "Anything that *can* go wrong *will* go wrong." We should be glad that people building our bridges and airplanes have this attitude. It drives them to anticipate problems and avert them before they kill us.

Years ago, I learned an important corollary to Murphy's Law, which I'll call Hayes-Roth's Dictum: *A disaster anticipated is a disaster averted.* In studying emergency preparedness, I found that many organizations create detailed disaster response plans, practice them periodically, and keep them "fresh" on a nearby shelf so they can be quickly employed when one of the anticipated disasters occurs. In interviewing these crisis response planners, I was amazed by an almost universal finding: the anticipated disasters didn't occur, even though several other ones did. So the organizations learned that the real value in their disaster preparedness planning was in the planning know-how they learned, not the actual plans themselves. If the organization could plan efficiently, it could usually develop a good plan relatively quickly in response to an actual disaster.

In business, I often took this one step further, to what I might call the *Proactive Approach to Murphy:* get Murphy before he gets you. If the actual disasters that occur are not the anticipated ones, but are nearly always surprises, one could further reduce the range of real disasters by anticipating more possibilities. Even if one did occur, having been anticipated and planned for, its impacts would be greatly mitigated if not entirely minimized as a consequence of being a predicted event. Further, if we could anticipate and forestall or minimize most or all of the events that otherwise would prove really disastrous, we'd be robbing Murphy of maneuvering room.

To get Murphy, as it were, we have to engage in the opposite of wishful thinking. We have to be uncharacteristically negative, to postulate that things go seriously wrong, and then force ourselves to uncover plausible ways things could really turn out that way. An example[10] will help. Suppose we plan a family vacation to visit a South Pacific island, to go scuba diving, and to stay at a lovely resort. The plan consists of getting to the airport, catching a series of flights, collecting our baggage at the end, and taking surface transportation to the hotel. The plan then incorporates daily activities, a reversed travel itinerary, and a return to home. To get Murphy, we first posit negative outcomes, ones that differ from expected in undesired ways. Here's a short list of such mini-disasters:

1. Our clothes don't arrive.
2. Our scuba equipment is lost.
3. Our dive computers don't work.
4. We arrive days late at our destination.
5. The hotel is full on our arrival.
6. Our child has to leave the island immediately.
7. I'm unable to dive.

---

[10] *One* of the book's many reviewers thought this example wasn't sufficiently "significant" to warrant the careful analysis being recommended, but he agreed that "important" plans, such as military operations, would clearly benefit from this kind of treatment. I think the example is more easily understood by a broader audience than a military example, and that is why I continue to use this example.

8. My wife's prescription dive goggles aren't available.

9. An emergency in the US requires one of us to return.

10. The airline cancels our flight.

Given any list like this, we convert each conjectured negative outcome into a plausible causal chain that could actually produce that outcome. In some cases this takes some creative thinking, but usually it's surprisingly easy. In fact, it's usually easy to generate multiple plausible causal chains. Here are some examples of how this process works:

1. Our clothes don't arrive

    a. ← bags are mishandled in transfer, or

    b. ← bags are left at our departure airport, or

    c. ← a bag breaks open and contents fall out, or

    d. ← bags are mislabeled at departure and shipped elsewhere

2. Our scuba equipment is lost.

    a-d same as for 1.

    e. ← thieves steal equipment, or

    f. ← other passengers mistakenly collect our equipment, or

    g. ← scuba equipment, being heavy, is held back for later flights

3. Our dive computers don't work.

    a. ← pressure problems in baggage compartments broke them, or

    b. ← their containers were rudely dropped, or

    c. ← their batteries are dead

4. We arrive days late at our destination.

    a. ← we arrive late for our first flight and lose our seats, or

    b. ← our first flight departs late and we miss a connection, or

    c. ← air traffic controllers strike for better conditions, delaying flights

5.   The hotel is full on our arrival.

    a. ← reservations were overbooked, or

    b. ← hotel occupants overstay the hotel's expectations for them, or

    c. ← the hotel claims no knowledge of our reservation

6.   Our child has to leave the island immediately.

    a. ← the child develops a dangerously high fever, or

    b. ← the child requires medical treatments not available on the island, or

    c. ← the child gets a rash on the flight and is refused admittance by immigration

7.   I'm unable to dive.

    a. ← my nose is congested and I can't clear my ears, or

    b. ← I find the conditions treacherous and frightening, or

    c. ← I fall, cut myself, and have a large exposed wound

8.   My wife's prescription dive goggles aren't available.

    a. ← they break in transit, or

    b. ← their containing bag doesn't arrive on time, or

    c. ← she cleans them before packing and mistakenly leaves them behind

9.   An emergency in the US requires one of us to return.

    a. ← my boss calls and demands that I return, or

    b. ← a key relative becomes deathly ill, or

    c. ← civil disasters occur at home and our property must be defended

10. The airline cancels our flight.

a. ← due to financial difficulties, the airline reduces its schedule, or

b. ← the aircraft needs maintenance and no substitute is available, or

c. ← the company goes bankrupt and suspends operations

When you look at this list, it's amazing anybody takes exotic family vacations, isn't it? None of these conjectured causal chains is particularly implausible or contrived. Travelers around the world have collectively experienced all of these kinds of problems with some regularity. Individual travelers, on the other hand, especially those with low frequency of travel experiences, have probably incurred at most one or two of these causal chains. As a result, individuals don't generally have the wisdom that comes from experience to *expect* these kinds of problems. For this reason, we want to force ourselves to be creative, to imagine the undesirable, and then to make it plausible.

It should be obvious that there's no limit to the number of problems we can imagine or the number of causes we could invent to produce them. The next amazing thing is that we can often readily invent solutions to each of these potential problems. That is, we can anticipate problems *and* insure against them, in various ways. The general tactics we employ to counter the conjectured problems and their causes are these:

I. Block the causal chain by undercutting something it depends on.

II. Mitigate the loss by purchasing insurance to compensate for it.

III. Prevent the causal chain's ultimate negative effect by implementing a redundant one.

IV. Assure the expected result by guaranteeing necessary precursors are in place so that actions taken will reliably produce expected results.

Let's consider how these four different tactics might work to insure the vacation comes off as planned. I'll show how the four tactics work on causal chains 1a and 3a. Hopefully, you'll feel the excitement that comes from mental jousting with Murphy and try a few more cases by yourself. This up-and-back with potential disasters reliably improves your expected outcome and, at the same time, deepens and expands your knowledge and wisdom.

1a. Our clothes don't arrive *because* our bags are mishandled in transfer.

   I.   Block the causal chain by undercutting something it depends on.

> What conditions enable or permit the *mishandling* of bags? Clearly, we have to give control of our bags to those who would mishandle them. So we could disenable the mishandling by not relinquishing control of the bags *or,* alternatively, we could relinquish control to *other* people than those who would mishandle them. This suggests two ways of undercutting something the causal chain depends on. Now we must conjecture a way to achieve our ultimate goal while also achieving the new objective of undercutting the link causing failure. Specifically, we might:
>
> (i) Carry our luggage on-board the plane, rather than checking it.
>
> (ii) Entrust the bags to a shipping company to be sent ahead of time.

   II.   Mitigate the loss by purchasing insurance to compensate for it.

> This tactic advises us to assure that an unexpected negative outcome doesn't cause the total loss of the plan. We can purchase insurance in various ways that would become activated if we needed it. Here are two ways to insure against the loss.
>
> (i) Purchase baggage loss insurance that would allow us to buy whatever we need at no out-of-pocket expense.
>
> (ii) Buy whatever we need at the destination.

   III.   Prevent the causal chain's ultimate negative effect by implementing a redundant one.

> This tactic advises us to assure a plan by incorporating multiple actions that produce the same desired results. All of that duplication is redundant, but redundancy in key causal chains can assure the desired result. Here are two examples of this type of redundancy.
>
> (i) Divide the travelers into two groups, taking different flights; split each person's clothes into two minimally satisfactory

subsets, and ship one half of each person's clothes on the two different flights.

(ii) Buy extra clothes and ship the redundant clothes ahead of time to the destination.

IV. Assure the expected result by guaranteeing necessary precursors are in place and actions taken will reliably produce expected results.

Using this tactic, we must make sure that things actually do work the way they are supposed to. How can we assure that our bags go with us, wherever we go? Here are two approaches that will assure that result.

(i) Carry our bags onto the plane and put them in overhead storage bins.

(ii) Purchase extra seats on our plane for our bags, and belt our bags into their own seats.

Hopefully these examples give a good sense of the creative thinking that results from this jousting with Murphy. Here are a few more cases to repair the plan deficiencies revealed in our negative thinking about it. We'll apply these repair tactics to problem 3 and causal chain a:

3a. Our dive computers don't work *because* pressure problems in baggage compartments broke them.

The four plan-failure-prevention tactics are *undercut, insure, assure with redundancy,* and *assure reliable* effectiveness. Applying the four tactics to the breakage due to pressure, we get the following four plan changes:

I. Pack the computers in pressurized cases.

II. Buy less expensive back-up computers and carry them on board.

III. Reserve rental computers at the dive destination in advance of traveling.

IV. Keep the computers in our immediate possession as we travel exclusively in pressurized environments.

In short, getting Murphy before he gets you is about using our knowledge of how things work to find ways out of fantasized problems. Simply assuming and asserting that our plans will fail produces a powerful, emotional, motivating effect on our thinking. We get very creative when we've failed, even hypothetically. Then, by systematically creating plausible chains of events that would actually cause the hypothesized problems, we can apply explicit operational procedures that I have called repair tactics to formulate new and improved plans. The new plans prevent or work around factors we initially overlooked. We initially chose to ignore factors that Murphy could employ to harm us. Well, the power of our knowledge and reasoning is such that we can anticipate him and thwart him, before he has a chance to do that to us. In this game of ploy vs. counter-ploy, we avert disasters by anticipating them. That leaves fewer and fewer kinds of surprises to bring us down.

Model, Predict, Expect

Thinking efficiently means that we get desired results with minimum costs. How do we actually do this, given that we operate in complex and dynamic environments with numerous partners and against numerous competitors? In a nutshell, we do this by pretty accurately anticipating the likely outcomes of our possible actions and choosing in the current circumstance the alternative that has the best expected net outcome. This basic idea of iteratively choosing the best available action underlies all intelligent behavior. When an entity does this better and faster than its competition, it prevails or, more precisely, it has the greatest probability of doing so. When competition continues over a long period of time, with multiple participants and multiple contests, the likelihood of the information-superior entity prevailing becomes nearly certain.

The key imperatives of intelligent planning and decision-making are to *model, predict* and *expect.* Modeling means creating and exercising symbolic or analogue representations of important objects and their interactions. Models always make some things explicit, while leaving out much else. A model of my car that I use on a regular basis includes relationships among the accelerator and brake pedals, the gear selector and the automatic transmission, speed and fuel consumption, normal and abnormal sounds, etc. My model of the car is intuitive in the sense that it's not described in any existing notation, it's not fully conscious, and it's not analytically or experimentally validated. The automobile manufacturer's model of the same car is both more detailed and less intuitive. It consists of both numerical simulations and mathematical engineering equations. In fact, the manufacturer uses dozens of models of the cars, each focusing on the relationship and behavior of different components and different aspects. Even for things that we'd normally assume were subjective and intuitive, such as consumers' responses to shape, design, color and gloss, the manufacturer builds, validates, and continuously improves explicit, non-intuitive models.

Models describe how the world works or, more precisely, how we believe some things work and affect one another. Mathematics underlies many models. If we know that our car consumes 1 gallon of fuel for every 20 miles of city driving, we can use mathematics to infer that 200 miles of city driving will correlate to 10 gallons of gas consumed. If we want to carpet a room that's 9' by 12' (approximately 3m x 3m), and that a square yard (or square meter) of carpeting costs $30 for material and labor, we can infer that we will need to pay the vendor $360 to carpet the room (before tax). The arithmetic and reasoning needed to solve such problems becomes routine by the time we reach adulthood. We almost fail to notice that the math is providing a model that enables us to accurately infer how things work in the real world of commerce, in this case.

Other foundations exist for modeling and inference, and these are used in various disciplines. While nobody has found models that require the abandonment of math, many other types of models augment it in various ways. In Part II of this book, we'll deepen this discussion to explore some of the important technical underpinnings. For now, it should suffice to bring out the types of models in routine use by people and modern organizations. The following list briefly enumerates some important types of models:

1. Weather models.
2. Terrain models.
3. Traffic models.
4. Logistic models.
5. Product models.
6. Consumer behavior models.
7. Chemical models.
8. Finite element models.
9. Statistical models.
10. Terrorist behavior models.
11. Battle models.
12. Political campaign models.
13. Financial models.
14. Ocean current models.
15. Global warming models.
16. Personality models.
17. Cognitive models.
18. Group dynamics models.
19. Religious models (e.g., of the afterlife).
20. Microeconomic models.

I could list many, many more classes of models. Each of them serves similar roles, but each is used in different areas of human endeavor and by different types of people. The models thus differ in what they refer to, what objects they comprehend, and what relationships they describe. They also differ in degrees of precision, physical scope, and temporal scale. The models differ in terms of scientific validity and degree of evidentiary support. Some models have gained increasing levels of credibility from having survived challenges, especially those that are in principle vulnerable to direct observation. In short, models represent a group's belief about how things work in a domain of interest. The more scientific the group's approach, the more the group subjects its models to empirical challenges and the greater our confidence in the validity of the model.

Models are used to *predict* things, such as the value of some interesting variable that will be observed in the future. Weather models, for example, try to predict the values of many variables, over many geographic and temporal dimensions. Will it be sunny, cloudy, or rainy at the park on Sunday when I hope to have a picnic? Will it be too hot? Will it be too windy? Automakers' models tell designers what it will cost to make a million copies of a conjectured part, how many of the produced parts will pass functional tests immediately after production, how long it will be before 5% of the parts fail, and so forth. Military combat models tell planners how many casualties will occur in the first hours of a campaign, how fast the offense can move, how many defenders are required to stop the offense from advancing past a certain line, and so forth.

A skeptical reader might say at this point, "Yes, but these predictions are frequently wrong." That is true. If models had to make perfect predictions all the times, we'd have no models at all. In spite of predictions being wrong often, we value any model that improves our odds. If we have no models, the answer to every question might as well be determined by rolling dice. Will it be sunny tomorrow? If the possible answers are "yes" and "no," we flip a coin and associate Heads with "yes" and Tails with "no." But even with very little knowledge, we can do much, much better. In Tel Aviv, for example, an excellent prediction results from the simplest of models: Sunny today implies sunny tomorrow; rain today implies rain tomorrow. If we are in Tel Aviv, we can do much better than chance by using this model, combined with current observations, to answer the question.

These simple examples reveal some important facts about prediction. We predict values of variables (or, more simply, "answer questions") by making inferences from models. To make inferences, we start by asking what is already known or observed or assumed to be true. Then, by some logical or mathematical or analogical process, we deduce the otherwise unknown values of interest. Different types of models combine with different types of inference to produce answers to our questions. The previous examples have shown how we can use arithmetic to predict how much money a carpet seller will demand, how sunny it might be in Tel Aviv tomorrow, how many variable speed windshield wiper controllers in cars will require replacement at the manufacturer's expense under warranty, and how many soldiers will die in combat.

Obviously, our models don't always predict values perfectly. In fact, they almost always err in their specific predictions. However, our models usually give us answers that are much closer to the actual truth than we could have guessed without them. This means that we usually care about how big errors are and, specifically, have a strong preference for small errors. If the temperature is forecast to be 80° F but actually turns out to be 82°, we consider that a much better prediction than one erred by 10° and better still than another that erred by 20°. The reason we value small errors is that ordinarily, when we must choose among available alternatives, the best choice doesn't depend on precise accuracy. Dressing appropriately for 80° means that we are likely to be comfortable even if the weather turns out to be 82° or 78°. But dressing for 80° doesn't work when the actual temperature turns out to be 70° or 60°. We want our predictions to be close, and rarely require perfect correctness.

In addition to preferring small errors, we want our models to be reliable, so that we can count on them always or mostly always giving us small errors. We usually prefer models that always err by a small amount over models that are often exactly right but frequently wildly far from the mark. When we use predictions to inform and affect our behavior, huge errors can produce disastrous consequences. We like our predictions to be close to the mark always.

Scientists and statisticians need ways to characterize the quality of predictions, and they need ways to reject bad models. Probability plays a key role in such analyses. The commonsense idea of probability works well in most cases to enable us to understand most of this work. Basically, probability measures how often one particular value of a variable occurs when we repeatedly sample it. The probability of tomorrow being sunny, for example, could be estimated by taking observations every day for the last year and computing the proportion of sunny days. With a more precise model, we can do much better. The Tel Aviv model, for example, uses only information about today, but it gives a better prediction for tomorrow. It estimates the probability as 100% of being the same tomorrow as it is today. Now, on its face, that can't be a true estimate of the probability, because there is some chance of an exception. But the model isn't reality, it's just a workable representation of how things work, and it gives probabilities for the alternative values of a variable of interest. Excellent models routinely make small errors and never make big ones.

In intelligent behavior, we use models and predictions to choose among alternative actions so that the chosen one gives us the best expected results. If the weather tomorrow is predicted to be sunny with temperature of 80°, we use that information to dress appropriately. Only a fool would wear woolen clothes and a heavy topcoat. It would be wise, under the circumstances, to wear cotton clothes and short sleeves. As another example, if the auto manufacturer has three alternative designs for the same component, it should choose the one that gives the best expected performance over the warranty lifetime at the lowest possible manufacturing cost.

Repeatedly, in many contexts, in many interactions, we must identify which alternatives are open to us and choose which to exercise. Will we wear wool or cotton? Will we use a large-scale integrated circuit or solder together multiple medium scale components? Will we deploy overwhelming numbers of troops or rely on fewer, more mobile, and more agile units? Will we try to minimize fat intake or eat a moderate amount of fat? Will we exercise in the morning or after work? Will we take the freeway during the morning commute or travel on surface streets? Life presents an endless set of questions that give us opportunities to do better or worse. When we make these choices consciously, we imagine each option and use our models to predict the likely outcomes. Good models with good inference methods yield good predictions. Good predictions give us better estimates of what outcomes will result from each alternative we consider. We are thus able to get better outcomes by choosing and then implementing the option that leads to the best predicted outcome.

I said that the three key imperatives were to *model, predict,* and *expect.* The first two functions suffice to enable us to choose alternatives that give us best expected results when we use them repeatedly to make every decision. One thing that should be nagging at you, however, is the suggestion that individuals or organizations continually decide everything they will do based on such thoughtful analyses. Of course, most of the time, most people, and most organizations behave like the weather in Tel Aviv: they do tomorrow whatever they do today. Habit, routine, standard operating procedures (*SOPs*), or whatever you want to call norm behavior does not seem to involve continuous deliberation and constant striving to optimize behavior. If people had to choose every action based on an explicit optimization of alternatives, we'd be overwhelmed by a huge amount of analysis. In some organizations, this type of behavior is ridiculed as "analysis paralysis." The antidote for such paralysis most frequently prescribed is termed the "ready, fire, aim" process. In that process, quickness is highly prized. This means players get better results by quickly implementing any reasonable alternative and then fixing any attendant problems. In contrast with the predictive and proactive approach to intelligent behavior, this approach emphasizes observing results to infer corrections that future actions should incorporate to move ever closer to optimum results.

These two approaches lie at opposite ends of a spectrum reflecting different design choices about one should consider information and analyze options. Based on different choices, decision-makers can assess information before or after implementing the chosen action. Every reasonably intelligent organization uses a blend of these approaches. While it's obviously silly to defer action indefinitely, it's just as silly to defer selectivity among alternatives based on current knowledge and predicted outcomes. What this contrast really reveals are two additionally important success factors: *speed* and *control.* We are competing with others, so we can't just sit around contemplating our navels. We are trying to produce physical results in a complex, dynamic environment, so we can't just assume that our actions have the effects we anticipate them to have. In the fist case, we have to limit our contemplation so we act swiftly. In the second case, we have to look for important indications of success and failure and use these to change our ongoing actions to produce results that get closer and closer to what we want. Together these processes determine how well we continually adjust our behavior to improve outcomes.

Both concerns, speed and control, are adversely impacted by complexity. Complexity arises from our needing to consider too many things, in too many possible combinations, with too many probabilistic events. It doesn't take much to create extremely complex problems. The so-called "traveling salesman" problem provides a good example. If a salesman has to visit each of his customers in a large area, he would want to minimize the time he spends in transit. Unfortunately, he'd have to consider all possible sequences of customers to find the sequence with the lowest total transit time. If he has N customers, the number of possible sequences is called *N factorial*, is written *N!*, and is computed by multiplying N times N-1 times N-2 ....times 2 time 1. Even 10! is a gigantic number, and 20! dwarfs the capacity of any computing system to evaluate. Many problems are as hard as this "traveling salesman" problem, so we cannot possibly be expected to optimize all or most of our daily actions.

Even in the ready-fire-aim approach, we are faced with exceedingly complex problems, such as which results to observe, how to analyze these observations, how often to do these analyses, which changes in behavior to implement, and how often to change instructions and implement new guidance to others we work with. Trying to determine optimum answers to these questions runs into intractable problems akin to the traveling salesman problem. So, the only intelligent thing to do is to reduce complexity through simplification so we can implement more and better feedback cycles.

Expectation is the capability that underlies this practical approach to reducing complexity. Having selected actions to perform, we use our models to tell us how things will work and what we should *expect* to observe. Furthermore, we can determine in advance which observations would signify serious errors in our predictions and which of these would warrant immediate attention. For example, the automotive manufacturer selected a component that it expected to fail once per thousand units in the first year, so expects a thousand failures among annual sales of one million. This corresponds to about 85 units per month. As long as components aren't failing much more than that, the manufacturer can pretty much ignore design and manufacturing alternatives for that component. 200 failures in the first month, on the other hand, should raise the alarm. Ignoring that discrepancy from expectation would expose the manufacturer to potentially huge losses over the product's lifetime.

In business, these ideas have been built into a management approach called *management by exception,* sometimes referred to as *MBE.* Under MBE an organization permits its components to operate mostly independently, but requires each entity to monitor key measures and report exceptions to higher levels of management promptly. This has two great benefits. First, it means that most elements of the organization can make decisions locally, without coordination, and that increases speed. Second, it significantly reduces the volume of information that flows through the organization. This gives each decision-maker more time and allows that time to be focused on information of greater significance. These benefits multiply and produce much higher levels of swift, intelligent adaptation.

Our ability to expect results and their associated observables makes these benefits possible. Once we know what actions we intend to make, we can plug those into our model and infer expected results. Our model also tells us how the expected results should manifest in observations we can make. We can also determine how deviations in actions, assumed conditions, or expected results would appear in these observations. We can determine which differences in observed results signify important deviations. We can then focus our energies and resources on monitoring the events that would signify important discrepancies. We can strive to detect significant *expectable* but *unexpected* indications. Thus, we can pretty much limit our activities to (1) doing what we planned and (2) monitoring our expectations. Any time and energy we save by limiting our efforts in these ways, we can apply to understand observed discrepancies, improve our models, investigate new and different alternatives, and improve our execution by reducing performance errors.

In sum, intelligent use of what we know determines what we achieve. The knowledge we use to make and evaluate plans resides in our models. We use these models to answer "What if?" questions. Once we've decided what to do, our models tell us what to expect and, most importantly, what indications we should look for to indicate that our models were wrong. All such activities are complex computationally, so require intelligent approaches to obtain excellent results with highly constrained analyses and resources. The more efficient we are, the more important things we can consider to an appropriate level. Nobody and no system can consider every alternative, at every moment, to a level required to optimize results. Efficient thought means doing more of the important things better than the competition. The enormous complexity underlying intelligent decision-making creates a competitive arena where information-superior entities can easily surpass competitors by huge margins, considering thousands more appropriate alternatives, at rates hundreds times faster, to levels tens of times deeper. Hyper-beings have the computational resources and skills to excel at these tasks. This accelerates their rate of separation from ordinary creatures and organizations.

Collect and Assess Evidence

Intelligent systems, as we have seen, depend fundamentally on their models. Models often differ in terms of the size and frequency of errors they make. We have thus far considered using models primarily in a proactive and predictive mode. In these uses, the models enable us to choose among alternative actions those that give us the biggest "bang for the buck." We need to consider now how we know which models to *trust*.

Intuitively, we all realize that we shouldn't trust people who lie and we should trust people who constantly make predictions that prove true. The same logic applies to models. The models we trust are the ones that prove their usefulness over and over again. If a model makes predictions that we can routinely confirm, our credence in it increases. Models that consistently lead us astray are best abandoned.

Scientists have worked out a discipline for evaluating models, and statisticians have contributed theory and techniques to assist them. In brief, scientists like to run *controlled experiments* to assess models by testing whether predicted effects occur. Usually in a controlled experiment, a model predicts that applying some treatment to one group should produce an effect in that group that differs significantly from what occurs in the other group without the treatment, *i.e.* the *control group.*. Statistics are used to validate this hypothesis, by determining when the measurements observed on members of the two groups differ by an amount that almost certainly can't arise merely by chance. This complicated logic enables the scientist to reject the "null hypothesis" that the two groups are indistinguishable on the variable measured. Having controlled all differences except for the treatment applied in the experiment, the scientist then concludes the treatment produced the effect the model predicted. Ta dah! The model is confirmed!

Ah, but beware. Science has shown repeatedly that confirmed models are not necessarily *correct*. That is, observations might prove consistent with our predictions for many possible reasons. Every intelligent being wants to use models that have excellent predictive track records: small errors, low frequency of errors. Scientists seek *valid models*, models that accord well with reality in that they consider the key factors, in the right relationships, and correctly predict how one state of affairs evolves into the next. In science, confirmation theory attempts to tell us how much we should believe any model, based on the experiments we have run and the alternatives we have considered and rejected. In a few words, we can never assume our model is valid, but the more times we subject it to opportunities to fail and the more alternatives we compare it to, the more credence we should place in it.

So, intelligent systems need to collect and assess evidence. Controlled experiments constitute the best known processes for gathering evidence that sheds light on hypotheses. All other means of evidence collection and assessment provide less reliable and less useful information. In all cases, we take as evidence observations that accord with observables a model predicts. In many cases, people reason *postdictively*, arguing that observations we've already collected are readily *explained* by the model. In this case, they suggest we should assume particular conditions existed in the past from which the modeled state evolved to yield the results observed. In short, when observed data align with what the model *might have predicted*, we take it as some evidence supporting the model. In every case, however, models must be vulnerable to disconfirmation. That is, we don't consider a model confirmed if it could just as easily explain every possible observation. Without vulnerability, models gain no credibility from apparent confirmations..

In business and government affairs, it's sometimes possible to run controlled experiments. Direct marketers do this all the time, for example. They run different advertisements for the same product, experimentally varying the photograph, the headline, the text description, the package, and the price. Even small differences in any of these factors can have an order of magnitude (10X) effect on consumer response. The marketers don't have models that reliably predict which choices will produce the biggest effects. For these reasons, direct marketers have learned that collecting and assessing evidence is a vital aspect of efficient thought.

In other types of activities, intelligent organizations have systematized experimentation, data collection, and analysis. Marketers and advertisers do this routinely and base multi-million dollar campaigns based on the results. Training programs in business and the military are tested for efficacy, and they often find huge differences among alternatives. If we are resource-constrained or competing in tough environments, we'd better be checking our models. Is the world working as expected, giving us results consistent with our predictions? When events disconfirm our models, can we modify them or find alternative models that explain and interpret results better? When data violate our expectations, our models are broken and we'd better fix them.

Learn from Experience

If the world operates as we expect, there's not much we can learn. We might increase our confidence in our model, but as the confirmation theorists point out, even that's risky. When we are getting some of what we want, we may be on the right course, but obviously we're not doing every necessary to get full rewards. On the other hand, when we clearly fail, we should rejoice: this is an unquestionable opportunity to learn something new and to improve our subsequent results.

As previously mentioned, failure can be emotionally painful, but this seems to be a genetically inherited spur. We don't like failing, and we dwell on ways to prevent it in the future. The previous section on getting Murphy before he gets you described tactics for improving plans that mentally simulated failures could stimulate. If we assume that we never make logically faulty plans, we can see that even simulated failures can reveal to us weaknesses in our models, ways that we overlook possibilities, or ways that we make unwarranted assumptions. Models comprise our beliefs about how things work. They should not overlook possibilities. They should not make unwarranted assumptions. Ideally, they would include and employ just the elements of knowledge that are necessary and sufficient to predict and explain events of interest. Of course, no one has models that can do this 100% of the time, so opportunities to learn from experience are virtually unlimited.

There are two important questions in learning from experience: *when* we should be learning and *what* we should be learning. With only a little simplification we can answer these both with a single sort of observation: when things don't work well, we need to learn why not. We need to improve our performance by conjecturing things that should work better. We need to experimentally test and assess the capability of the improved model, incorporating the new knowledge, to confirm the model's ability to address the observed failure as well as its ability to do at least as well as the unimproved model on previously tested challenges.

The plan improvement tactics discussed in the earlier section coordinate with knowledge improvement tactics. That is, I have identified several practical procedures for conjecturing new knowledge required to address plan failures. Even when plans are not evident, actions that lead to undesired consequences should trigger efforts to debug the implicit beliefs underlying the actions. Of course, if actions are being generated without regard to reason, a whole other set of problems is evident. We'll focus here on behaviors that emanate from intention and reason which, nevertheless, get the wrong result.

In the previous section, we identified four tactics for repairing buggy plans. These four tactics are repeated here:

I.   Block the causal chain by undercutting something it depends on.

II. Mitigate the loss by purchasing insurance to compensate for it.

III. Prevent the causal chain's ultimate negative effect by implementing a redundant one.

IV. Assure the expected result by guaranteeing necessary precursors are in place so that actions taken will reliably produce expected results.

There are two completely different approaches to implementing these tactics. In the first approach, as illustrated when discussing Murphy, we apply what we already know to design a plan that won't be afflicted with the identified failure. We did this for fantasized failures, but we could of course do the same things in response to actual or predicted failures. In the second approach, we change our model in a way that we conjecture would cause our same old planning approach to produce a more robust plan, one that would be invulnerable to the causal failure chain identified. These two different approaches may have the same effect in the case of the one plan or activity being considered. But changing our model affects all future plans and also creates a more urgent need for model validation. If we intend to change our model, we'd better be prepared to collect and assess evidence, even being prepared to abandon the conjectured change when it fails to accord with evidence.

When I first discovered these constructive ways to change models, I found a striking similarity to what the mathematician Lakatos had described in his fictional play among a math teacher and his students, entitled "Proofs and Refutations."[8] In his play, he compressed 100 years of math in a small area of geometry, to show how people eventually learned from a series of failures. The failures that arise in math come from people finding counterexamples to theorems. The counterexamples satisfy the premises of the theorem but not its conclusion. The problem is not in the logic, as this is usually sound. The problems lie in the *concepts,* what people include and exclude within the named categories that the theorems pertain to.

In my own research on this topic, much of it done with Phil Klahr at the Rand Corporation, I realized that similar kinds of problems underlie much of operational thinking[9, 10]. Failures in performance can often be traced to weaknesses in concepts, not to weak or incorrect reasoning. What one must learn from failures is what distinctions to make, how to categorize things, and how to assure that inferences reliably predict real world results by avoiding over-generalizations and unwarranted assumptions.

Let's consider some examples. Tactic I blocks a failure by undercutting something it depends on. If we reason our bags were lost because we entrusted them to somebody (who, in turn, mishandled them), we could change our concept of baggage handlers to distinguish between trustworthy and untrustworthy handlers. At that point, we'd incorporate into our model that bags arrive on flights manned by trustworthy people. We might incorporate into our model that bags do not arrive on flights manned by untrustworthy people. We might place the workers of the airline that had mishandled our bags into the latter category. In any case, we'd be changing our model so that predicting our bags would arrive with us would now explicitly depend on a new distinction of trustworthiness. We would have undercut the failure now attributed to giving bags up to an untrustworthy person. Each of these model changes is conjectural: some will prove effective and valid, while others may be difficult to show effective or difficult to validate.

In the second tactic, we mitigate the failure-induced loss by somehow insuring against the loss. In the case of losing our bags, we could modify our concepts to distinguish insured *v.* uninsured bags and then predict low-loss baggage delivery only for insured bags. This would mean that each time we wanted to achieve low-loss baggage delivery we might require insured bags as a prerequisite. As an alternative, we could add to all expected results a concept of *riskiness* and risk-mitigated-through-insurance. Then we could impute riskiness to each plan, perhaps based on the number of people, transportation legs, number of bags, etc. At this point, if we required a low risk plan, we'd have to incorporate some actions designed to convert the imputed riskiness into an acceptable level of risk-mitigated-through-insurance. Our model might already incorporate knowledge of what types of insurance can mitigate risk, so that we'd simply need to include actions

56

consistent with prior knowledge to achieve the desired effect. In any case, we would have now expanded our model to incorporate distinctions about riskiness and risk mitigation, creating a need for plans to address these distinctions in ways that satisfy the mitigated-risk constraint.

The third tactic requires us to incorporate redundant actions to assure that no single fault might nullify the plan. We could also change our model to make a new distinction between non-redundant-and-vulnerable on the one hand and redundant-and-reliable on the other hand. We could then require that each action in every chain be deemed redundant-and-reliable, or we could require that each important aspect of the intended results be itself redundant-and-reliable. In the former case, we'd want to have each important intermediate result achieved by a redundant-and-reliable method or accomplished multiple times, thus being itself redundant-and-reliable. In the latter case, we would require such redundancy only at the final step. Of course, reliability can be achieved in different ways, with different costs, and different levels of assurance. The point here is to illustrate how one expands and modifies the model to incorporate conjectured improvements so that these, in turn, can be subject to experimentation and exposed to potential repudiation through failure.

The fourth tactic addressed problems by guaranteeing that sufficient conditions obtained. These conditions would suffice to assure the reliable performance of each action in the plan so that each action's expected effects would follow reliably. To illustrate how this approach works, consider how it would modify concepts to incorporate a distinction between reliable-performer and unreliable-performer. In this case, we could require that only reliable-performers perform planned actions, thereby eliminating failures arising from unreliable-performers. If we could actually identify reliable-performers, this would go a long way to guaranteeing that each plan step worked as expected. Businesses employ this distinction frequently in the ways they qualify, select, and compensate suppliers.

Each of the tactics described above can be readily implemented in procedures that people or computers perform. Specifying such procedures in executable code would require considerable details. For now, hopefully I've conveyed a few important ideas in a simple way. First, failure is an opportunity to learn and improve. Failure motivates us, it compels us, it begs us to find things we can change to avoid it in the future. We can change what we do, to work around failure or to undercut it or negate its impact.

Alternatively, we can change what we believe, modifying our categories and concepts based on new distinctions, so that we don't again think in ways that let past failures intrude. This approach is powerful and cumulative. Over time, out distinctions are sharpened to serve the needs for avoiding over-generalizations and implicitly relying upon implicit and unwarranted assumptions. The new concepts join older ideas in our mental models. We continually subject our concepts to experimental use, in plans, predictions, explanations, and failure analyses. Concepts that work well become trusted and relied upon. The others ultimately are rejected, and these are relieve of responsibility for any further information processing duty. In this way, experience continually drives a culture of beliefs, subjected to evidence, that prove their mettle or disappear.

Efficient Thought: The Superior Decision Loop

We can pull together the principal functions of efficient thinking into eight steps, each supported by a world model that represents our best understanding of how things work. Figure 2 illustrates these components.

The world model provides the knowledge that an intelligent being uses to interpret events, generate candidate plans for improving situations, and select the most attractive candidates for execution. Throughout the life-cycle, the intelligent being learns from experience how to change the model to yield higher levels of reliability. Updates are made to the world model in four of the eight steps. In step (1) our observations about positions, speeds, and other current status update variables in the model to reflect these simple types of information. In step (2), we interpret our observations in light of expectations to determine surprises or key data that disambiguate important uncertainties for us. In step (7), we adjust our own model to take into account the fact that we are adopting a new plan we intend to implement. Finally, in step (8) we make changes to our model when we realize it's wrong or when we rule out previously plausible interpretations. Our failures and experiments stimulate and inform such learning.

The other four steps in the efficient thinking loop lead from our situation assessment processes through (3) setting objectives that might respond to threats and opportunities identified in that assessment, (4) generating plans to achieve these, (5) projecting how these candidate plans would probably work, and (6) selecting among the plans based on their expected outcomes and probable costs. Efficient thinking considers the things that matter for success,

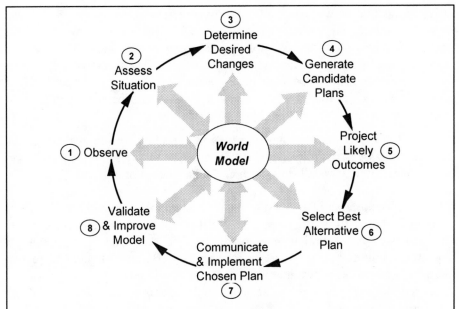

Figure 2. Efficient thought employs eight key functions supported by a world model.

The eight steps are numbered in a typical sequence, though in most complex organizations all eight steps operate in parallel. The intelligent being (1) observes what's happening in the environment, (2) assesses the situation for significant threats and opportunities, (3) determines what changes would be desirable, (4) generates candidate plans for making those changes, (5) projects the likely outcomes of those plans, (6) selects the best plan, and (7) communicates that plans to key parties and implements it. Throughout, the intelligent being (8) validates and improves its model. The model supports all eight activities, although only steps 1, 2, 7 and 8 directly update and modify the model.

uses the best knowledge and reasoning processes, and continually adjusts knowledge and behavior to approach ideal results.

Conclusion

This chapter has focused on two halves of the power behind intelligent beings, *what* they think and *how* they use their limited information-processing resources. Each entity that finds itself in a competitive environment should strive to behave in ways that will maximize the probability of its success. Whether consciously or unconsciously, the intelligent being wants to act consistent with beliefs that reliably predict how things work. Moreover, it wants to use models containing those beliefs to choose actions that have higher probabilities of producing better results. In these ways, the intelligent entity wants to use models that enable it to plan and perform actions that reliably succeed.

Because life is dynamic and complex, no one has time to evaluate every alternative, assess it fully, conjecture all possible lessons learned, and experimentally assess all knowledge. Quite the contrary, our extremely limited information-processing resources allow us to consider only a tiny fraction of our alternatives. Most of the time, we simply depend on things that worked in the past to work acceptably well in the future. Intelligent systems that manage by exception maximize the resources they can devote to potentially important innovative opportunities. MBE allows them to reduce the number of things they instrument and observe, the number of messages they send around, and the time they must spend to process bits of no significance.

Efficient thought results from honing concepts to work in practice. To sharpen our concepts, we need to focus as much energy as possible on learning. Learning enables us to identify new concepts and make improvements to existing models that have potential to improve future outcomes. Humans, as a species, do much of this both intuitively and formally. Hyper-beings pursue building and improving models as their prime objective, the way honeybees build hives and store honey as theirs.

4. Information Superiority

The US military has incorporated information superiority as one of its central strategic pillars for more than a decade. The visionary leaders in the Defense Department realized that rapidly advancing information technology would transform military doctrine and tactics in revolutionary ways. So many technologies and innovations were spewing forth that radical change seemed certain. GPS systems enabled each vehicle or soldier to know its precise location. This precision could enable attackers to use fewer, more precisely aimed weapons. Small numbers of attackers could more devastatingly attack a fixed target than could the large numbers and carpet bombings of previous generations. One bomb exactly on target was infinitely better than a thousand bombs that just missed the target. Stealth technologies allow units to avoid detection as they approach. Packet radio communications provide secure ubiquitous voice and digital services. Digital geographic information systems combined with real-time intelligence analysis and fusion techniques mean that every tank and aircraft can see its own position in a combat situation, can identify friends and foes, and can employ cunning routes and tactics. The list of innovative advantages coming from the ability to manipulate bits intelligently goes on and on.

Organizations have understood the advantages of information superiority for millennia. Powerful monarchs, prelates, and political leaders have employed spies to collect information about their rivals. They have used various means to spread disinformation that would mislead their opponents. They have used propaganda and advertising to cajole and nudge individuals, ethnic groups, and international audiences to align their personal models with sponsored ones. Nations have enlisted their students, missionaries, and professionals to be "cultural ambassadors," to spread the values and viewpoints of the dominant players.

Every advantage that arises from bits, models, and beliefs plays some role in information superiority. In its broadest sense, information superiority means winning the battle of the bits. Of course, information gains its material advantages through its effect on actors who rely on that information to surpass competitors, gain resources, and improve their knowledge and control. Even reducing unpredictability in the behavior of others can contribute to information superiority. The better I can predict your behavior, the better I do at planning and achieving predicted results. In short, dominant entities want to control information the same way the Air Force wants to control the air and the Navy wants to control the seas. Information superiority means you are a step ahead, better prepared, more potent, and more in control than your competitors.

In this chapter, we will look at ways actors gain the advantages of information superiority. These ideas work for an individual, a small business, a large business, a government agency, or a transnational hyper-being. I will focus on about a dozen things you want to be able to say to your competitors, and you really don't want them saying these things to you. Let's start with the first nasty jibe, "My Decision Loop is Better than Yours."

My Decision Loop is Better than Yours

Many people who have studied decision making have identified the feedback loop as the foundation for adaptive behavior. Of course, the most hackneyed example of this kind of loop involves a thermostat, controlling a furnace (or an air conditioner). In the case of the heater, the thermostat turns the furnace on when the observed room temperature falls below the desired, or "target," room temperature more than a small allowable amount. When the temperature rises a wee bit past the target temperature, the thermostat shuts the heater off. This is called a "loop" because information goes into the thermostat, from the thermostat to the furnace, from the furnace to the room in the form of air temperature, and back to the thermostat in the form of measured air temperature. Information flows around this loop continuously, causing the thermostat to turn on or turn off the furnace depending on the difference it computes between the target temperature and the measured room temperature. This particular type of decision cycle is called a closed loop feedback system. The only information the system uses to regulate its behavior consists of the recently computed difference between measured and target air temperature.

Investigators in various fields ranging from psychology to organizational design have noticed that adaptive systems must evolve into more complicated, structured, and differentiated structures as they grow in size and operate in increasingly complex environments. The most typical organizations you find operating in complex environments use a hierarchical system structure with a small number of parts to produce a wide variety of appropriate behavior. In a hierarchy, the highest members usually worry about big issues at coarse levels of detail, such as what's our mission, how much can we afford to spend, and what policies should we impose.

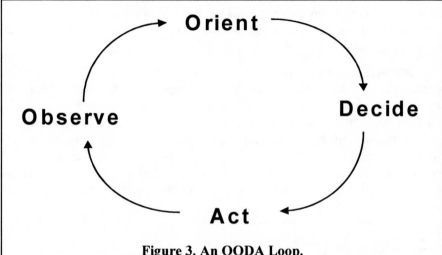

Figure 3. An OODA Loop.

Boyd's OODA loop emphasizes four principal steps in adaptive behavior: observing the environment, orienting towards important factors, deciding what to do, and then acting to change one's situation. Each entity in an organization may need to compute these loops while trying to mesh their decision-making and acting.

As you move down the hierarchy, mid-level managers take responsibility for particular functions or important sub-goals that their subordinates will undertake. In business, these intermediate levels address tasks such as profitably producing and selling a particular product, designing and manufacturing a new starter motor for the car, or other similar tasks. In the military, mid-level decision makers take responsibility for determining how to defend a particular installation, capture a key target, or defeat an enemy unit. In government, mid-level managers are responsible for delivering various services to the public at adequate levels of customer satisfaction while keeping costs within budget.

At the lowest levels of organizations, individuals, machines, or small ensembles interact with the environment directly, apply resources to transform material or persuade a customer, as required. The hierarchy works both top-down and bottom-up. In top-down mode, high-level mission objectives translate into tactics and tasks and ultimately into movements and operations. In bottom-up mode, units measure and report their results, interpretations, and lessons learned to superiors, and this process repeats up the levels. Although few organizations operate 100% hierarchically, nearly all highly evolved entities competing in complex environments exhibit mostly hierarchical structure and function.

Regardless of how many levels of hierarchy, all intelligent entities operating in dynamic environments have to adapt their behavior continuously in response to feedback. The entity as a whole uses a decision loop to do this, and each subordinate entity in the hierarchy uses a decision loop in its own area of responsibility. These loops have been given different names by different researchers in different disciplines. They have been called control cycles, feedback loops, test-operate-test-exit TOTEs, and observe-orient-decide-act OODA-loops, among others. I'm going to refer to them as decision loops.

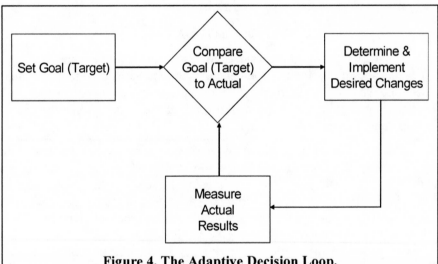

Figure 4. The Adaptive Decision Loop.

Adaptive decision-making requires changing future behaviors to get better outcomes by reducing differences between the actual results and the goal or target. This feedback loop enables adaptive control.

The purpose of the decision loop is to alter one's results to move them continually closer to one's goals. "Make the room temperature close to the target I set." That's the purpose of the thermostat. Warm-blooded animals have a similar "thermostatic control" loop to keep their body temperature close to a healthy target. The Federal Reserve employs a similar decision loop to keep the "temperature" of money on target for the overall economy; they focus on the rate of growth in the money supply as the measure of temperature. In these and other cases, the basic idea is hugely important and stunningly simple: notice a difference between actual and intended results, and fix it. "Ready, fire, aim."

In spite of its essential simplicity, different ways of implementing this kind of loop can produce enormous differences in actual outcomes. To perform perfectly, we'd need perfect information, instantaneous computation of discrepancies between desired and actual situations, immediate computation of the change in behavior that would optimize future results net of any implementation costs, immediate communication of this change to all affected participants, perfect understanding of the intended change by those participants, and perfect implementation of those changes by them without additional delay, unintended effects, or unanticipated costs. The perfect decision loop would be a thing of beauty. It is, like Venus, a fictional ideal.

Actual decision loops in the real world usually perform so far from perfect that perfection isn't much of a guide. The reasons decision loops are usually mediocre are many, but here's a short catalog:

> Decision makers receive imperfect information. It's errorful, incomplete, inconsistent, and tardy. People in organizations often believe they benefit from withholding some information or can avoid penalties for fudging data. In many organizations, people inflate reported results, so that others receive bogus information.

> Decision makers don't immediately understand situations accurately and usually are very slow to identify correctly deviations from expected results that implicate performance problems they should address. Businesses seem to rise and fall together, like ships with the tides. A business that is doing badly when others are too is usually headed by an executive who attributes the poor results to "externalities." Under-spending of resources doesn't usually get noticed, although it indicates problems as much as overspending does. Decision makers try to spot significant deviations, but they usually feel they are looking for needles in haystacks. Generally, when untreated problems

persist troubles mount, eventually overwhelming decision makers with bad news. At that point, they react.

➢ Decision makers take a long time to decide how to intervene, and then they usually guess. Most decision makers are distant from the day-to-day details of business, government, or warfare, so the information they receive is aggregated, abstracted, filtered, and distorted. Even when it becomes clear that plans are failing, executives doesn't know exactly how to fix things. Their personal models are too simple. Their organizations don't collectively create and operate a comprehensive model of the environment. The people chosen by the organization for its rapid reaction task force consider some factors, ignore most details, and guess which of a few remedies would work best.

➢ Rather than communicating the intended change immediately to all affected participants, most decision makers engage in "window dressing" and other image-management activities in the hope of softening the implied message that the organization is screwing up or, more precisely, that the executive is failing. In many large organizations, public relations concerns rank at the top of the executives' personal agendas. Even if the ship is sinking, the leader will suggest that the problems are less severe than they appear, they were anticipated rather than brutal surprises, they have external causes rather than resulting from the organization's behavior, that they can be easily remedied, that the leadership team understands them and knows just how to fix them, and that the rest of the troops trust the leadership and will shortly swing into unified action to make the leaders' visions come true. Needless to say, with this kind of communication agenda, the people in the organization charged with actually fixing what's broken rarely get straight talk and clear signals.

➢ People asked to implement changes rarely understand their tasks and roles perfectly. Requests reach doers from decision makers who have very different contexts than the receivers. Instructions usually leave out many details, under the assumption that the receivers will fill in the missing details in a predictable way, *i.e.,* in the way the requesters intend. With extensive practice on repeated scenarios, people can learn to minimize communication problems. But many tasks and contexts in real life are different than ones extensively planned for and practiced. As a result, requesters usually don't specify tasks adequately, and people receiving tasks have difficulty fully appreciating the nuances of the challenging situations handed to them.

> People don't actually do many things exactly in accordance with some idealized statement of intent. They do a little bit more or a little bit less, they are a bit fast or a bit slow, and they usually create many side-effects that may or may not be material. They aren't maximally efficient or effective. They incur costs that decision makers didn't anticipate. They accomplish results somewhat different from what we ask them to do.

Because there is a huge range of possible results between the idealized objectives of a plan and what real organizations accomplish, decision making is never just "fire and forget." Intelligent beings have to continuously reevaluate how their current plans are working out and iteratively cycle through decision loops. They do this at every level of the functional hierarchy. The loops produce decisions that are intended to be mutually reinforcing and collectively effective. Loops at one level turn goals from a higher level into actual planned tasks, and these tasks are in turn given as goals to performers further down the hierarchy. Almost every aspect of these interlocking loops is fraught with errors and deviations from the ideal, as considered above. Nevertheless, this is how the intelligent entity moves its many parts, iteratively, closer to where it wants to be. It isn't pretty, but it's the best design Nature has found.

Now that we realize how sloppy most organizations are in their decision loops and how many cycles are required to deal with internal errors as well as external stimuli, we can readily appreciate the advantages that would accrue to an information-superior competitor. Any competitor that operates decision loops with greater speed, reduced error, better knowledge, more effective communication, and more reliable translation of goals into actions will out-think and out-perform its competition. If my decision loops are better than your decision loops, ¡hasta la vista, baby!

My Sensors are Better than Yours

In any competition, the decision loop operates on inputs that originate with sensors. The thermostat gets information on air temperature from a thermometer. If the sensor is off, the whole process will be off. As we move into more complicated environments, the sensors become more sophisticated and potentially powerful. The potential for errors increases, too. A familiar range of errors in sensing occurs in people's vision. While the average 20 year old with excellent vision sees 20/20 (can see at 20 feet what those with good vision can see at 20 feet), a large number of people have a range of defects, including near-sightedness, far-sightedness, astigmatisms, and so forth. In the case of human vision, there's a steady statistical deterioration with age. Few adults over 40 years of age see 20/20 without corrective lenses. In contests based on excellent vision, the odds clearly favor the young with defect-free eyes.

In business, many different types of systems and devices play sensing roles. These range from devices used in manufacturing processes to measure inputs, operating characteristics, and outputs, to devices embedded in products that observe how the products perform, to daily reports on sales, deposits, and debits, among others. Businesses cannot properly correct and control their behaviors if their sensors don't provide sufficient information.

In military competitions, sensing is the start of surveillance, reconnaissance, and intelligence. Modern militaries sense in many spectral arenas, including visible and infrared light, audible and inaudible sound, thermal and chemical emissions, and electromagnetic frequencies where radio and digital transmissions occur. The modern military wants to be able to see and hear everything significant that its opponents do and say. The US military, for example, watches and eavesdrops using airborne and space assets, as well as using terrestrial techniques to intercept telecommunications.

The quality, quantity, range, and coverage of sensors combine to determine the full scope of what the organization can see, hear, and otherwise observe. On these dimensions, the more the better. On the other hand, the volume of data generated by sensors often exceeds the organization's ability to process it. In such cases, too much of a potentially good thing becomes negative. Advanced sensors used by sophisticated organizations minimize the problem of information glut by incorporating means to remove redundancy, extract important features, and filter out noise or other inconsequential data. Such sensor processing and filtering significantly improve the value of sensed data and at the same time increase the likelihood that the organization will be able to digest and exploit significant sensed data.

Sensors can also be cued to focus on detecting significant events, rather than monitoring a broad range of mostly unimportant events. We may know, for example, that emissions in a particular frequency range implicate an important activity, while others can be ignored. Cueing the sensors to put all of their power into monitoring the important interval can increase their ability to detect events while also assuring that they no longer report volumes of data about irrelevant frequencies.

When we have sensors that can be located and focused in such a way as to give us accurate, timely and comprehensive reports on categories of events we identify as potentially significant, we have a great sensor system. In competing with others, hyper-beings realize that their supremacy is both enabled by the superiority of their sensors and limited by any inability to detect important events quickly and reliably.

My Information is Better than Yours

Information consists of meaningful bits of data, *i.e.* data that make a difference. Streams of bits that never change nor ever differ from our expectations don't tell us anything. On the other hand, data that disconfirms an expectation signifies that the world is not behaving the way we believed it would. Decision makers rarely operate on raw sense data. Instead, they almost always receive processed reports intended to give them information that signifies something important.

My organization can outperform yours if it uses better information than yours. There are several important ways in which information quality can differ. These include correctness, completeness, consistency, currency, conciseness and significance. Let's refer to these desirable qualities as *5C+S* and consider each one in turn.

Correctness. We want the information we receive to reflect accurately the situation it claims to describe. Its assertions should be correct. Information should make explicit pertinent limits of knowledge, uncertainty, and irreducible error, so we don't act on a false sense of precision. For example, if we last observed an aircraft at a particular location two minutes ago, at the present time we have only two choices. We can either report assuredly where it was two minutes ago, or we can specify a rather large envelope of where we believe it probably is now, up to some confidence factor. Errors, false precision, underestimated uncertainty, and misinterpretations are a few of the enemies of correctness. Information that doesn't even consider or estimate these enemies has built-in limitations.

Completeness. When we receive information, such as a progress report on a mission, we don't know what hasn't been told to us. The supplier of a report makes many choices about what to include and what to exclude. We want a complete report, one that assures us that it doesn't fail to disclose material information. The report provider must have a good understanding of the recipient's context, including current beliefs and sensitivities, to know what the recipient would consider material. Such understanding is hard to achieve. Report providers continue to filter information, hoping to provide most of the best information for their readers. Incomplete information is fundamentally limited. Completeness depends on the context of the recipient, and that context changes continually. Unless provider and recipient continually resynchronize and share contexts, the provider probably does a poor job on completeness.

Consistency. We want the information we receive to be consistent, otherwise we don't know which parts to trust and which to dismiss. Consistency is challenging however. In simple identification contexts based on mutually exclusive categories, for example, we consider any report that assigns each observation to one of the categories as plausible and internally consistent. In most complex environments, however, reports are full of fuzzy terms, with overlapping meaning. We receive reports that tell us, for example, demand is "erratic" but "increasing." We interpret this by ascribing a meaning, hypothesizing a state of our world model, that makes both terms plausible. For example, we might assume that the measured demand is a random variable whose mean is increasing week to week. Generally we don't treat such reports as inconsistent, because it seems too hard, and it questions the value of the report. It could well be the case that demand is not increasing, but is simply erratic and over some recent period randomly trended upward. The worst case for a receiver is to be told two contradictory things or to be told two things that imply contradictory things. This occurs frequently in complex environments, however, because reports come from parties with different perspectives or access to different sensor data. Every inconsistency is a direct challenge to each element of the reported information. Superior organizations focus on finding and eliminating inconsistencies, where possible, before they propagate. Having tried to eliminate inconsistencies but failed, the sophisticated organization understands that the inconsistency reflects a flaw in its own models or its processes. The superior organization works against the human tendency to sweep inconsistencies under the rug, hoping they won't be noticed and won't prove important.

Currency. Information is perishable, just like good vegetables. If we don't consume the information while it's still fresh, it loses value quickly. "Current information" is somewhat oxymoronic. From the moment information is written and reported, it's no longer totally current. It's aging fast. The time taken to get information from the stimulating events to the decision maker is called *latency*. In dynamic environments, our entire decision loops have to cycle a bit faster than the environment changes in order for us to continually improve our performance. If the information latency by itself is a significant proportion of the cycle time, we'll have trouble completing the cycle fast enough. Late information is no information. Currency is a vital aspect of information value. In competitive arenas, currency is often more valuable than money.

Conciseness. Samuel Clemens famously apologized to his correspondent for sending such a long letter. He just didn't have the time to write a shorter one. Of course, good writers know that rewriting, editing, and polishing significantly shortens prose. Like a bad musical composition, information can have "too many notes." Why is conciseness so important? There are two key ways in which it helps the intelligent entity succeed. First, by eliminating unimportant, redundant, or superfluous bits, it reduces the volume of information the recipient must process, thereby reducing the consumption of cognitive resources. Second, by using fewer words to encode information, the writer exercises greater selectivity, choosing *le mot just* for every important idea. This increases the clarity of the message received and the impact it has on the receiver. Saying everything that needs to be said as briefly as possible is an art that few people find easy. As a result, organizations are awash in verbiage, mumbo jumbo, and ambiguous messages.

Significance. Significance is so important, it demands a word that doesn't begin with commonplace C. Information matters, when it does, because it tells us something we don't know, don't believe, or don't really want to hear. Important news is often unpleasant, because it signifies that we've got a problem or we need to change our plans. The greater the impact, the more we have to change, the more significant the information. When an information supplier knows the decision maker's context, he or she can appreciate the significance of various types of possible events. When the organization has an important mission underway that depends on some critical assumptions, the mission and the organization are vulnerable. If events occur that undercut the assumptions or negate them, the mission is jeopardized. Who can forget the failed US mission to rescue hostages from Iran using helicopters in the desert?

Windstorms undercut the low altitude visibility such missions depend upon. As with other dimensions of quality, suppliers can appreciate the potential significance of their information only when they understand the context, the missions, and the vulnerabilities of the decision makers they report to. This isn't possible through telepathy. If you want your suppliers to expedite significant information, you need to share your context with them and work with them to identify vulnerabilities that their information might address.

In short, giving others high quality information isn't easy. In most mediocre organizations, people and systems aren't measured on the quality of information they provide or penalized for flooding the system with low quality information. Yet such measurement and reward schemes are obviously vital to achieving information superiority.

I Process Information Better than You

Organizations differ in how effectively they process information. Mediocre performers fall below ideal levels in many ways. The 5C+S criteria apply to information processes as well. Deficiencies in correctness, completeness, consistency, currency, conciseness and significance also occur in the imperfect processes that receive information, manipulate it, and propagating it to others. For example, processes that make errors, overlook and omit bits, produce inconsistent answers, deliver results late, obscure important facts in reams of reports, and unselectively report on everything rather than focusing on important aspects all tend to weaken the organization relative to efficient thinking competitors. Beyond these parallels with the 5C+S features of good information, processes have other aspects that can afford advantage. These are power, simplicity, reliability, agility, and bang-for-the-buck. Let's consider each of these in turn.

Power. In manufacturing, processes transform materials, adding value, ideally making more desirable products with each successive step of work. In information processing, the materials being processed are bits, and each successive step of work supposedly increases the value of that information for its intended recipients. When we transform physical materials, we can use slow, dull and manual tools, or we can use fast, sharp, power tools. In processing information, we also seek tools that work fast and precisely to remove unwanted bits, reveal important aspects, and yield polished results. Statistical analysis tools, as one example, can transform large amounts of data into concise, accurate, model-based interpretations. GPS tools, as another example, can determine where we are and show that to us in a graphical context that enables us to comprehend easily a set of spatial relationships between us and others in the environment. Customizable triggers and alarms allow the users to describe conditions of interest so that the information processing systems can monitor the environment and notify the user as soon as they detect an occurrence of those conditions. The more our information processes employ power tools, the fewer of our resources are consumed by low-value work.

Simplicity. The KISS principle is a favorite among operational managers: Keep It Simple, Stupid. Simple processes have fewer parts, easier steps, and fewer dependencies on external factors. In contrast, complex processes create playgrounds for Murphy. Murphy can find many ways to bring down a complex process, since it has so many dependencies on assumed conditions that make it vulnerable to nasty surprise. We want our information processes to be as simple as possible, without sacrificing effectiveness. Techniques for achieving simplicity include standardization, formalization, composition, specialization, automation, programmability, and intelligent control. We give brief expositions of each of these now:

- **Standardization** reduces variation in the components by requiring that they all belong to the same narrowly specified family.

- **Formalization** yields written procedures that improve our abilities to accomplish analysis, communication, training, and performance review.

- **Composition** reduces the number of steps by replacing a sequence of steps with a single function that accomplishes the same transformations. This reduces the number of process steps and the number of transitions that work must make.

- **Specialization** is accomplished by allocating dedicated processors to different types of processing, which enables us to train them better or apply more effective machinery.

- **Automation** allows us to replace human processors by machines, thereby reducing variability and often reducing cost. When we reduce variability in any step, it reduces the range other steps must handle and simplifies the task of interfacing one step's processors to others.

o **Programmability** means that we can change our processes by following a well-defined process at a higher level of information processing. If we can easily re-program processors to meet challenges presented by changing conditions, we increase agility without incurring the costs and problems associated with acquiring and implementing new processors.

o **Intelligent control** enables us to get desired results, simply, by employing the "ready-fire-aim" procedure, relying on our feedback mechanisms to adjust subsequent aims to approach optimality quickly. The more intelligent the control mechanisms we employ, the simpler the task of producing desired results. Such control means that we need not expend huge amounts of time and resources trying to perfect the underlying process steps.

Organizations that employ these simplification techniques appropriately create processes that work reasonably well, over a broad range of circumstances, much of the time and cost a lot less than complex alternatives. Organizations that have a predisposition toward complex processes open the door to Murphy, who finds an infinite number of ways to surprise them, slow them down, and hit them with performance problems and maintenance costs.

Reliability. We want processes that give the right results nearly always. There are many analytical ways to measure reliability, but they all boil down to telling us whether we get good enough results often enough. If our processes produce too many errors, or occasionally produce errors that are way too big, or sometimes just refuse to work, we've got reliability problems. Information systems that rely on many devices, connected by many networks, accessible by many outsiders, have frequent problems with reliability. In recent times, the rise of Microsoft's monopoly in desktop computing has driven many organizations into positions of extremely low reliability. Any successful virus or worm attack on Microsoft's products rapidly propagates around the world and brings down huge numbers of personal and corporate computers. Many decision makers moved toward single-vendor systems in the naive hope of achieving improved reliability through concentration, standardization, and commoditization. If all the parts lived in isolation or had limited vulnerabilities, this vision might prove credible. Given the high degree of insecurity associated with commercial software products accessible over the Internet, the evidence indicates that current approaches to homogenizing equipment and software decreases reliability. Needless to say, when I'm competing with others, I like to know their systems are vulnerable and mine are not. Reliability can be improved in many ways and also degraded in many other ways. If our processes don't work when we need them and don't work as they're supposed to, they become real liabilities, creating additional vulnerabilities.

Agility. Many processes are honed to do a small number of things well. That is, after all, the first law of industrialization. Only advanced industrialized enterprises learn that they can achieve much higher results by shifting their processes quickly to new opportunities or altering them as required to meet particular competitive threats. In business, the mantra of "agile manufacturing" has been the goal for a decade or more. Reducing downtime between products and mixing different products in the same space, on the same equipment, during the same day can greatly improve productivity. In military operations, the changing nature of threats and missions has created analogous pressure to improve agility. This requires improved means of assembling *ad hoc* coalitions, comprising *ad hoc* units, capable of employing *ad hoc* tactics, deploying quickly, and possessing sufficient smarts to adapt their operations in real-time. For centuries, militaries trained to achieve victory in slow combat, force on force, where the numeric ratio between attackers and defenders predictably determined outcomes. Those days are gone. Today's military organization must be able to put together processes appropriate to momentary challenges. The organization must be programmable, which means that effective, specialized processes will need be composed from off-the-shelf components and controlled intelligently.

Bang-for-the-Buck. All physical entities have limited resources, and all processes consume resources. Resources spent doing one process aren't available for other purposes. Clearly, the organization wants to get the most valuable results it can from whatever resources it must expend. "Bang-for-the-buck" measures the ratio of value produced to cost incurred.[11] Determining value produced is often harder than measuring cost incurred. In fact, most accounting practices focus exclusively on the costs of activities rather than the value those activities produce. In information processing, the situation is extremely bad. We have computers, information bases and files, reports,

---

[11] Accountants use many different measures to assess bang-for-the-buck. The most common include , *operating margin, profit, return on investment, return on equity, return on assets employed,* and *economic value added.* These all seek to show that the organization's activities produce more value than they consume.

email messages, real-time displays, decision support systems (DSSs), etc., yet most organizations have not even begun to grapple with the question of how to concentrate resources on producing high-value information. Some information systems though have become associated with measurable results, because they have been built into enterprises that can directly relate performance to the 5C+S of their information. Examples of these modern systems include:

- o supply chain management systems that manufacturers use to coordinate the flow of parts to reduce work in progress and inventory, thereby reducing capital tied up financing goods not yet ready for sale;

- o business-to-business exchanges, which allow buyers to reduce costs by having near perfect information at all times about suppliers' offerings;

- o and financial alerting systems that individuals and businesses can employ to monitor for conditions of interest and signal them when opportunities arise.

In all of these examples, people can see they are saving or making money through the use of 5C+S information. In business intelligence and military intelligence, however, the current practices attempt to substitute "volume of information" for "value of information," creating systems that actually flood processes with too much information, causing those processes to degrade and to propagate more low-value information down the line. When we understand how to increase value, we begin the process of moving to higher bang-for-the-buck processes, and these give us great advantages over competitors.

My Models are Better than Yours

My ability to get what I want depends on my models of how things work. If I want people to like me, I should behave nicely to them, because I believe people like those who act kindly toward them. If I want to dominate someone, I might try to bully and intimidate that person, because I believe intimidation leads to submissiveness. Using knowledge from social sciences, I could instead build up their dependency on me, by repeatedly giving them things they want, and then use my power to withhold these things from them in the future to bend them to my will. These examples from everyday, personal life can be easily recognized. But our models cover many different spheres of interaction and influence. Businesses develop models of consumer preferences, how their products work, how their processes transform materials, and how money spent in different geographies, different parts of the business, or different functions influences outcomes. Diplomats develop models of cultures, leaders, and other diplomats, so they can reason about likely effects of potential plans and about the ways their actions would be interpreted and responded to. Military thinkers model the systems that states and organizations use to operate their businesses, cultural institutions, civic affairs, and military operations. They use these models to look for "centers of gravity," points of enormous leverage and potential vulnerability, which they can attack in case of combat.

Our models power the thinking that leads to our choices. We choose A over B because we believe, for some reason, that A gives us a preferred outcome. If my models improve, I get better outcomes. If my models are better than yours, the smart money bets on my success in competitive contests with you. A recent news article about the highly effective Wells Fargo illustrates these points[12]:

> Wells Fargo & Co. has become so good at predicting consumer behavior that it practically knows what customers want before they realize it themselves. The San Francisco bank's secret: Net technology that it developed in-house last year. Every transaction—whether it's over the phone, at an ATM, in a bank branch, or online—is collected and combined with personal data that the customer provides. Wells crunches the info and models behavior to come up with prospective offerings, like a low-cost second mortgage—just at the right time to coincide with a life-changing event. The result: Compared with the industry average of 2.2 products per customer, Wells Fargo sells four.

I Think More Efficiently than You

Efficient thought means processing information in ways that achieve superior results. As we've previously considered, this means understanding a situation, considering possible future actions, evaluating them, selecting ones that will get best possible results, and them continually adjusting actions in light of feedback. Two competitive organizations might have identical models and comparable information yet still show a statistical superiority of one over the other. The quality of those doing the thinking can be a dominant factor. If

---

[12] *Business Week,* November 24, 2003.

the people in my organization understand efficient thought and know how to optimize their thinking, they will out-think the competition. Most organizations today have only a rudimentary understanding of efficient thought, and they don't hone their processes or the skills of their thinkers. Mostly, organizations use simple, primitive methods for choosing their decision makers, such as success in a previous operation or interpersonal charisma. Furthermore, few organizations yet employ artificial intelligence directly in their thinking, although this is certainly appropriate in many arenas. Lacking a clear understanding of what efficient thinking is and what it requires, organizations don't measure it, reward it, or select for it. Worse, many organizations informally punish efficient thinkers, as these people often identify problems that others prefer to ignore or suggest new plans or processes that would require new organizations or changes in roles, responsibilities, and status. There's a reason messengers beg not to be shot: most people and most organizations are resistant to change and somewhat deaf to bad news. The organization that cultivates efficient thought, makes people feel safe to express their thoughts, and continually responds appreciatively to new and improved ideas has a dramatic advantage.

I Communicate and Control Better than You

In order to make things happen, decision maker need to communicate information, policies, intentions, constraints, permissions, tasks, requests, and plans throughout the organization. The measure of communication quality is not how much is said but, rather, how much of what should be understood is received by the right parties, correctly interpreted, and promptly translated into appropriate behavior changes. Anyone with children or pets can immediately see the difference between what is said and what is received and implemented. A famous Far Side cartoon by Gary Larsen shows this comparison succinctly in two panels. In the first panel, a pet owner is scolding his dog Ginger over some bad behavior. The second panel reveals what the dog is hearing, "Blah, blah, blah, Ginger, blah, blah, blah, Ginger…" While we like to think things work better in organizations, I have some doubts.

Most organizations are afflicted by two phenomena that cause messages to be misunderstood. First, as in the children's "telephone" game, messages transform as they pass from one entity to another, often becoming seriously altered before finally arriving at the end of the line. Second, people have motives and positions they are trying to protect. So each person who has a chance to "spin" the message a little, often torques it slightly to make the speaker seem more important or to enhance the speaker's portfolio. At the same time, the recipient suspects the motives and wisdom of the planners as well as the motives and self-interest of the speaker, causing the recipient to interpret the message in a context of "why is the speaker saying this to me?" Finally, recipients have their own agendas, position in the hierarchy, and sense of importance and authority, so that they selectively hear and interpret messages from their own contexts and with their own perception of opportunity *v.* threat. If the people in the organization aren't trusting and good listeners, messages don't have the intended or desired effects.

Communication underlies the rest of the control loop as well. Messages must be formulated and transmitted that report on how plans are working out. These reports can be biased to make the sender look good or to minimize attention. Delivering bad news, as we have said, can prove lethal to messengers. Even with good feedback, control may perform poorly, because it's slow, coarse, or ineffective. Although we may be correctly receiving reports of failure, we might be unable to effectively adapt our behavior. Organizations that implement effective processes of continuous improvement usually prove very successful. To attain that type of excellence, they work hard to create processes that insure participants see and hear the truth, consider several good alternatives, quickly and thoughtfully choose actions that appear likely to improve outcomes, convey those changes clearly, and motivate participants effectively to implement those changes and report accurately on the effects they produce.

You Can't Fool Me

If every great strength is also a weakness, the vulnerability of the intelligent being is its sensitivity to misinformation and deception. Villains through history have exploited this weakness against a spectrum of opponents. A good lie can be a powerful weapon. It causes the opponent to mistakenly modify its model, which can bring down an entire enterprise or nation. Because the intelligent being depends so vitally on information and model-based thinking, deception is a regular tool of those seeking power. Deception ranges from little white lies and exaggerations to misdirection, misrepresentation, misattribution, and other big lies. Children learn the value of lying at an early age, because lies avoid unpleasant consequences. Almost everyone learns that there's safety in ambiguity, so people often fuzz-up statements of responsibility and accountability. "The exact cause of the poor results can't be known for certain, because so many factors were at work." "The market went up (or down) because investors were bullish (or bearish, optimistic, happy, worried, surprised, concerned, etc.)."

In a world where outcomes depend crucially on information, the opportunity to gain power through manipulation increases. Recipients thus benefit from applying procedures to information that qualify it and assess it, just as buyers of other goods do. We need insure that our information suppliers know what we value, so they can have a chance to give us good stuff. Then we need to make it clear to the suppliers that we value veracity highly and will impose severe penalties on lies, deceptions, and selective omissions. We will need to implement real audits of our information suppliers, run periodic investigations, and follow up on our promises through rewards and penalties. We need people to know they can't fool us, and we need to avoid being fooled.

Depending on the nature of our competition, the rules of engagement, and the moral questions, we might work just as hard to deceive and manipulate our competitors. Entities that are never fooled and can fool their opponents at will attain significant competitive advantages. Understanding the processes used to improve one's confidence in its own information supply further reveals opportunities for Murphy to undercut that chain or for information warriors to take Murphy's place.

Trust Me

Now that we can see how suspicious an intelligent being should be of those providing information, it's apparent how trust works to leverage advantages and mistrust works to multiply disadvantages. When we get information form trustworthy sources, we ought to trust it. Otherwise, we'll waste resources and time vetting it without increasing value. Similarly, if we are given 5C+S information from sources we have previously learned to distrust, the value immanent in that information is wasted on us. The opposite types of effects also occur. So we want our organizations to be able to trust their information providers in order to increase their advantages. We also want recipients of our information products to trust and value them.

As a result, as organizations continue to compete in a world where information superiority grows ever more important, trust becomes increasingly important. Whole businesses may be brought down by acts that squander trust, as we have recently seen with Wall Street scandals. The foundations of empires can be eroded by mistrust and cynicism. When Microsoft announces it is emphasizing "security" and regularly reveals critical security weaknesses in its software, the savvy consumer begins to translate "trust me" into "this won't hurt much." When politicians repeatedly do one thing and say the opposite, the listener begins to translate this newspeak reflexively.

Companies, governments, and militaries can either magnify their power or undercut it based on the way they manage their trustworthiness. You can fool some of the people some of the time, but nobody can fool all of the people for very long. Organizations that cultivate trustworthiness and create a trusting culture of constituents inoculate themselves against the harmful effects that distrust engenders in the intelligent being. Trust amplifies the power of knowledge and the efficiency of thought. Superior organizations will eventually see the wisdom of measuring their constituents' behaviors on the trustworthiness dimension and publicizing objective measures that reinforce trust. In a world operating on superior information, trust enables superior organizations to communicate faster and more effectively and to cause constituents to listen, understand, accept, and act on what's said to them.

Work With Me on This

There are few things we can do alone. Every organization requires teamwork and cooperation. Extensive enterprises and hyper-beings achieve everything they do through the combined effects of many cooperating entities. In the industrial age, engineers thought through most processes, work was broken up and choreographed, and the sequence of process steps allowed people to combine their effects, serially, through time. Concurrent communication among tens or hundreds of participants was rare. It was also largely at odds with the basic approach to achieving productivity.

The rise of the information economy, the widespread availability of networks, improved means of telecommunicating, and innovative techniques for interacting with people on digital products have unleashed a torrent of collaboration. Collaborative technologies vary over a wide range, including among others: email; instant messaging; chat; webinars; decision-support-assisted conferences; and distributed cooperative design and engineering environments.[11] Because information is so important and quality decisions so valuable, superior organizations bring needed talent and capabilities to the problems, on an *ad hoc* basis. A good example of this trend showed up a few years back when IT experts discovered that they could throw urgent user problems into MOOs (nicely appointed chat rooms[13]) and allow problem-

---

[13] MOOs are MUDs built using object-oriented technology. MUDs are Multi-User Dungeons, on-line virtual worlds allowing many participants to explore and interact

solving experts to jump in wherever they felt like it. This had the nice effect of bringing just the right set of collaborators to the same place at the same time focusing on the same task.

This way of not organizing, not structuring, not sequencing work and not determining how best to optimize the experts' time reportedly led to a huge increase in problem-solving productivity. Before the organization adopted this approach, it found that challenging problems typically would take very long periods of time to solve. Difficult problems would move slowly through the organization, being transferred from one person to the next after frustrating each person for hours or days. With the new approach, tough problems are thrown into the experts' pen, as it were. These immediately stimulate and challenge the experts who can quickly combine their expertise and can collectively update their models based on new experiences. Working together to tackle a high-value problem <u>right now</u> and produce an expert result typifies today's information-superior organization.

As an example of how dominant companies are leveraging assets to improve collaboration, this recent report on IBM[14] provides a stunning lesson:

> Picture 300,000 of the world's sharpest workers brainstorming. That's how IBM views its intranet. The idea is that for every challenge, someone can come up with an answer. And IBM's intranet, one of the world's biggest, brings the team together, sometimes in groups of more than 1,000. Big sessions are known as Web Jams because of the jazzlike free flow of ideas. Other Web confabs are more intimate. They pay off not only in ideas but also in reduced travel. Web conferencing alone cuts expenses by $20 million.
>
> **The Payoff**: Cut $375 million annually off the training budget and another $20 million in travel expenses, thanks to Web conferencing.

Drive the Competition Crazy

When we consider how our planned actions will work, we usually employ models that predict how other actors will behave. Although we can't ever know with certainty how anything will behave, mostly our models describe

---

in different rooms. MOO technology makes it easy to furnish various rooms with handy tools that can augment visitors' capabilities.

[14] *Business Week*, November 24, 2003.

the main tendencies and acknowledge a range of statistical variation. We plan again these main tendencies. As we've discussed before, failures usually result from things not behaving the way we expected. It's particularly upsetting when opponents surprise us and defeat us by contravening our version of "the rules."

We begin to assume that our opponents have to follow the logic we've attributed to them. That's a dumb thing for any competitor to do, of course. In professional poker, as an example, the best players reliably beat others. They don't do this by getting better cards. They do this by reading the competitor's "tells," and by building up a pattern of their own tells that others begin to learn and master. Then, at a critical moment, the great poker players give a sign that's incompatible with what they've trained the competitors to recognize.

Driving the competition crazy is an excellent idea. It allows the superior organization to force the competitors into a reactive mode, trying to recover from one surprise after another. In business, there are many ways to drive the competition crazy: start a price war; introduce a new product superior to theirs; out-spend them on advertising; hire their best people; sell a product line to one of their competitors; publish the results of a comparison that favors your product; and so forth. In games of skill such as poker and chess, you drive competitors crazy by disturbing their concentration, leading them down garden paths only to surprise them with a bizarre and unexpected action, or feeding an impression of superiority that grows into complacency. In military competitions, you drive your opponents crazy by ignoring their superiority and focusing on their vulnerable "soft" targets, by breaking the rules, and by keeping them off balance with rapid-fire crises.

The more you know about the opponent, the easier you should find it to violate its expectations. Make the competition believe they can understand and predict your behavior, then pull the rug out, change your stripes, and throw 'em a Mickey Finn.

Get Inside the Opposition's Decision Loop

We've already considered how decision loops work, and why, to be effective, they must produce new actions somewhat faster than things change. When organizations don't feel intense pressure from competitors, they typically evolve "pretty good" decision-making processes. But "pretty good" doesn't cut it in intense competition. Your decisions and your implementations aren't just judged on vague abstract criteria. They either beat the competition or they don't. There's a reason why one player often dominates each niche: that player out-thinks and out-executes everyone else.

In intensely competitive arenas, each player has at least two foci for its actions: the environment and the other competitors. Thus, a business can offer the customers a price break, or it can attack the competition by buying up all critical supplies or signing exclusivity arrangements with distributors and retailers. Each time one competitor directly attacks another, it forces the victim to deal with a new problem. If the attacker can continue to inflict new problems faster than the opponent can deal with and recover from them, the attacker prevails.

Repeatedly making decisions, implementing them, and damaging an opponent, faster than the opponent can recover, is what we refer to as *getting inside the opposition's decision loop*. On a graphic display of events over time, we'd see the superior competitor responding to events and causing new events repeatedly, before the weaker competitor can complete its response to earlier events. The length of the attacker's loop would be shorter than the duration of the responder's loop. The superior adversary would close the loop multiple times, before the respondent would successfully close the loop once. The tempo with which impacts are delivered, repeatedly interrupting the opponent's efforts to formulate a response, measures the pace of conflict.

To the swift goes the prize. Because the time required to close a decision loop is totally determined by the organization's information processing system, we can see that information superiority translates directly into supremacy.

Summary
Information superiority deserves the importance modern organizations like the US Department of Defense have attributed to it. If one is engaged in mortal competition, the potential to dominate an adversary is directly related to how effectively we process information and whether we out-think the opposition. Throughout the natural world, individuals, organizations, nations and species are engrossed in competition, whether mortal or merely economic. All spheres have limited resources, and individuals in these arenas must best the competition to thrive. Homo sapiens has been using advanced information processing techniques for centuries to gain advantages over other members of the species and to extract advantages from the environment.

In the last few decades, it has become possible for humans to participate in far-flung organizations, to communicate with hundreds or thousands of collaborators, to receive vast quantities of data in near-real time, to apply teams of experts and supercomputers to decision loops, and to command and intelligently control distributed systems of people and machines to implement chosen plans with continually improving levels of effectiveness. These collective organizations achieve results in proportion to their information superiority. While most organizations are low on the learning curve for these capabilities, the information and communication technology (ICT) that constitutes their central nervous systems can readily support vastly higher levels of capability. When organizations put all the pieces together appropriately, they become distributed intelligent systems. In the next chapter we'll look into these systems to consider how it all works.

5. Distributed Intelligent Systems

The advantages of intelligence can be multiplied by scale and size. A single physical being is limited to a few meters in length, because the being's volume and weight increases as the cube of its length. Bones, muscle, tendons and tissue can't scale up to support that much weight. If we want to make an intelligent being that's *much* bigger, we need a different construction kit, based on a different architecture. Just as animals that fly have to change architecture as they increase in size, from the exoskeletal invertebrates to the skeletal vertebrates with feathered wings, our intelligent beings will need a whole different architecture if they want to reign supreme among gigantic competitors.

The way humans have historically scaled up their reach and competitive dominance is through empires. Although the exact structures and coercive means varied, the basic scheme had common elements. A central ruling authority, the emperor and the Senate say, had overall control. This authority would take as many of the empire's resources as it desired, and it would set policy, appoint regional leaders, and allocate wealth to those who played along. It would squash those who did not accede to its authority and supremacy. Communication and resources flowed from the regions to the central authority and back again, as needed, to keep the extremities aligned with the head.

These historical examples exhibit the key characteristics of distributed intelligent systems. We see different entities, spread through space, communicating via best available technologies, moving resources around to accomplish the goals established by the decision-makers. Over the last few years, however, the technological basis has matured for doing these functions extremely efficiently. As we have previously discussed, these systems can now operate nearly entirely as information-processing entities operating in a virtual world. Distributed intelligent systems no longer depend on physical presence, domination and control of populations, and massive accumulations of capital and other resources. In this chapter, we'll look at the information-processing nature of these systems and gain an appreciation for their essential properties. That will enable us in subsequent chapters to have a better understanding of the way these capabilities give rise to super creatures. We build up an understanding of the full architecture a bit slowly, starting first with the definition of *system.*

86

Systems

When engineers speak of a *system,* they have in mind a set of interacting parts that performs some intended functions in response to inputs. The system generally produces observable outputs, and we call the sequence of outputs its *behavior.* The system's behavior is determined entirely by its current state and the inputs it receives from the environment. Every interesting system has *memory,* and we refer to the contents of that memory as the system's *state.* As far as a system is concerned, its current state retains all important information about the system's past history. Only those experiences that alter memory can change how the system might respond to future inputs. No memory, no lasting effect.

Of course, the most interesting determinant of the system's future state is how the system processes inputs to produce outputs and update its state. An electronic calculator, for example, does the correct arithmetic operations for each button the operator pushes. It clears its memory when the "memory clear" button or "all clear" button is pushed. Otherwise it continues to accumulate results based on inputs it receives. Sometimes, the results of operations exceed the calculator's capacity to store or display numbers, and the machine will display an error message such as "E - - - - - -." At other times, the machine will be asked to make finer and finer distinctions, as when we repeatedly take the square-root of a positive number. Eventually, we ask the machine to make a distinction that goes beyond what its state can represent, and the machine will just say "1.0000000" as its approximation to the truth.

All *deterministic finite state machines* exhibit the same types of features. Such machines behave predictably, or *deterministically,* making a transition from one state to the next based on the input they just received and processed. They have finite memory and can't make an infinite number of distinctions. They reliably reproduce the same behavior whenever started in the same state and subjected to the same series of inputs. Actual machines incorporate various types of useful memory structures, such as high-speed arithmetic registers, push-down stacks for recording information when temporarily leaving one program and starting another, and random-access memory (RAM) for recording lots of data digitally. All practical computers behave deterministically, and nearly all exhibit a limited variety of behaviors.

More complicated systems can vary in several interesting ways. Some systems have, in principle, an infinite number of states. A Turing Machine, for example, can read and write information on a tape, and that tape may extend as far as required. Because the machine may utilize as much tape as it wants, the machine in principle can make an infinite number of distinctions. In such a case, the machine may actually work on some problems without *ever* reaching a conclusion. In fact, a simple Turing Machine can do surprisingly capable things, such as mathematics, symbolic logic, theorem proving, and problem-solving. Any system that can do all of these things might also be asked to solve some problems that just aren't solvable. In such a case, the system might work forever, fruitlessly trying, in effect, to find the end of an endless maze. We shouldn't consider the system's inability to terminate its fruitless pursuit as a defect. Rather, it reflects both a diligence in effort and an inability to assess its own predicament. In principle, we could enable a machine to know what we know about some unsolvable problems, so it could escape from some endless pursuits. Such an enhanced machine could pursue two tacks in alternating moments. It could systematically try both solving problems given to it and, alternatively, determining the given problems unsolvable. It would then work more like us, only tirelessly.

Systems can also behave non-deterministically, meaning that they might follow alternative paths probabilistically or somehow pursue multiple paths simultaneously. This enables systems to take on many interesting problems containing many related sub-problems. In these problems, one usually can't tell which incremental results will ultimately prove useful. We can't accurately judge progress until we find an overall solution, usually combining many partial sub-solutions. Systems that, in principle, can pursue all the possible solutions simultaneously can take on many problems that an ordinary person would find incredibly complex and extraordinarily burdensome. Non-deterministic systems, in short, eat up combinatorial problems that require the rest of us to try one combination after another until we exhaust all possibilities. Systems that pursue multiple paths in parallel don't really solve more or different problems than systems that can pursue only one path at a time, but we they seem conceptually simpler and more powerful. In the world of abstract but easily imagined systems, non-deterministic systems solve many problems that the rest of us find exponentially hard, unbelievably time consuming, and intractable. Regrettably, big, powerful, non-deterministic systems exist only in our imaginations. In the real world, where deterministic systems live, the bigger the systems we can implement, the bigger the problems we can solve. Because these real-world systems have practical limits to what they can do, many interesting problems won't yield to solution.

Systems can also have varied sorts of memory, that make it easy for them to structure complex tasks more simply or organize problem-solving more easily. Simple memory structures such as queues to keep items ordered, lists to build linked structures and graphs, or pushdown stacks to keep things in reverse order can simplify different types of assignments and related problem-solving procedures. Queues make it easy to manage traffic, for example, while linked lists make it easy to parse and analyze sentences. Pushdown stacks make it easy to solve problems hierarchically or recursively, remembering where you came from, and popping these memories off the top in reverse order as subtasks complete.

Systems do their work by having parts that receive inputs, determine state, and apply rules or procedures to determine how to behave. We might analyze a system in terms of its physical parts, its assemblies, its functional components, its power requirements, or any other interesting aspect. Systems that operate in the real work usually have principal purposes and secondary ones. A heating system, for example, has the principal function of maintaining room temperature close to the target setting. It has secondary purposes as well, including user interface functions, power management, forced air management, and installation mounts, among others. When information scientists look at systems, they usually discern and abstract as the primary view of interest how information flows to enable the system to perform its primary function. In the case of the heating system, this view would comprise the ambient temperature sensor, the set point, the thermostat that compares those two, and the on/off signal that flows back to the furnace. Many alternative views of systems are possible. Usually one view is appropriate when designing or operating a system, and a different view is required to debug why a misbehaving system is doing something unintended.

As we discussed earlier in the context of getting Murphy before he gets you, systems can fail for an uncountable number of reasons. Fortunately, systems most often fail for familiar reasons, as when a component fails, a communication line becomes disconnected, a power source disengages, etc. But the desired, predicted function of a system rests on many contextual assumptions that usually no one voices. Violations of these assumptions can bring the system to its knees. Complex systems have complexities that may have dependencies on both known and unknown factors. We can identify many of these by simply presupposing that the system fails and then identifying plausible causal paths that would lead to such failure.

In short, systems behave, usually to serve some purpose. They have means of sensing inputs, maintaining state information in memory, computing procedures or rules that determine the appropriate output and next state, and then updating the state accordingly and transmitting the output to the environment. The systems can become highly embellished with complicated and sophisticated sensory and perceptual systems or with multitudinous groups of amplified and specialized effectors. The systems can have huge numbers of parts and vast storehouses of knowledge and memory. Nevertheless, when we take the perspective that we should ignore all extraneous bells and whistles and focus only upon how inputs and state determine behavior, we have zeroed in on the essential *system*.

Intelligent Systems

You may not have noticed that the systems we just discussed had no special level of knowledge, expertise, or intelligence. The calculator is an interesting example. A modern cheap electronic calculator easily solves problems far beyond the capabilities of most mortals ever alive and more than all who lived a few hundred years ago. If we had a strict formal definition of intelligence, most people would wish to exclude a simple electronic device that can only perform a limited repertoire of calculating procedures. When we talk about *intelligent systems,* we will also exclude it. But to see why, let's clarify what intelligence means and what it entails.

Intelligent systems exhibit their intelligence by showing that they use what they know to adapt to changes in their environment. This means that they innovate new procedures to improve their outcomes, especially as required by changing circumstances. Suppose, as a trivial example, the user of a calculator noticed that one of the keys didn't work, so he chose a different key as a substitute. My calculator, for example, has several "memory" keys such as M+, M-, CM and RM. If I noticed that the zero ("0") key no longer worked, I'd be mightily impressed by the intelligent behavior of my calculator in quickly realizing that whenever I pressed one of the M keys in the context of other digits that I wished the calculator to interpret that M key as a zero. Of course, my calculator wasn't designed to adapt or innovate, so it's not going to do that. But if it did, I'd credit it with some intelligence.

Let's look into the three elements I ascribed to intelligence above: (1) uses what it knows (2) to innovate (3) to adapt. Adapting means it gets better results than it could otherwise, because the environment rewards the new behavior over the previous one. Innovating means changing the logic, procedure, or rules it uses, so that it processes familiar inputs in new ways that yield preferable behaviors. Using knowledge means making informed judgments about what might be good ideas, thereby making smarter guesses and smarter bets than otherwise possible.

When we talk to people, we can ask them why they do things, and they can often explain to us the knowledge they use and the reasoning they employed to create or recognize a promising innovation. Some computer programs can produce innovations as well, and we can inspect the logic they use to do this. In both cases, we can see how they use knowledge to innovate to adapt. Unfortunately, when other animals generate innovative behaviors, we have great difficulty discerning what knowledge they use or how they use it. We have trouble knowing how chimpanzees, for example, reason to solve problems experimenters throw at them. Nevertheless, it seems evident that many animals innovate, and the more they innovate, the better they get at it. Gregory Bateson described such improved innovative behavior in dolphins[12], for example. So, let's avoid pointless debate about which animals are intelligent and grant that many may be.

So any system that uses its knowledge to conjecture innovations that increase its expected returns qualifies as my kind of intelligent system. We can now ask what qualities these systems possess that the other kinds of systems don't. We notice immediately that the intelligent system looks at the way it produces its outputs and considers changing it. Why would it do that? Well, simply put, natural systems that could not continually improve their behavior didn't fare too well in dynamic and challenging environments. The lichen may not need to change its behavior, because it occupies an ample niche with few natural competitors. It needs only modest conditions to sustain, and these rarely change during its lifetime. We can't say the for mammals or humans, in particular. These critters evolved in challenging niches, with harsh and varying environments, full of competitors. These animals needed to survive by exploiting their wits. Wit enabled them to out-think their competitors and then to exploit their experience to improve their understanding and resultant behavior. Learning from experience assures that they know how things work so their behaviors achieve rewarding results with increasing frequency. Learning enables them to know the things they use to innovate to adapt.

If we leave the tissue and gray matter out of the discussion, what makes a system intelligent? The intelligent system must continually engage in learning, innovating, and experimentally determining what works and what doesn't. Each of these functions is vital. If it doesn't experiment, continually trying new things to discover what success or failure ensues, it can't make improvements necessitated by external changes. If it doesn't innovate, it tries the same thing over and over again. If it doesn't learn what works and how things work, it does no better than a coin-flipper would at trying to put together new behaviors. Intelligent systems, consequently, have memory that contains knowledge about how the world works and what effects actions produce. These systems also have means to formulate conjectures about hypothetical behaviors or procedures. These conjectures define candidate innovations the systems eventually must assess experimentally. Thus, intelligent systems have ways to represent new "programs" that the systems could execute as well as ways to translate programs into actual behavior. So while even Turing machines can store and execute programs, the intelligent system can modify its programs and generate new programs for its own use. Lastly, the intelligent system can execute programs in a mode that reinforces success and punishes failure. The intelligent system then increases use of reinforced procedures and the knowledge that produced them and justifies them. Concurrently, it reduces the frequency with which it performs punished procedures and the credibility it places in knowledge associated with those procedures. The intelligent system acts in its environment in a manner similar to the entrepreneur in a market economy. The system conjures up things that it hopes it can sell successfully to earn good profits, while it continually refines its understanding of what works and what doesn't.

One final point: intelligent systems comprise systems *plus* intelligence. So any system, regardless of its structure, organization, or processes can potentially apply for membership. To qualify as an intelligent system, it must perform four functions of (1) using its knowledge (2) to innovate (3) to adapt, while (4) continually improving its knowledge based on experience. Any system that does these, regardless of its composition, qualifies as "intelligent."

Efficient Thought in Intelligent Systems

In an earlier chapter, we explored the importance of efficient thought, information processing that uses best available methods to conjecture and execute behaviors that will attain superior results. It should be clear that the model-based eight steps laid out there provide one specific design for endowing a system with intelligence. Efficient thought gets better results in a specific way that allows intelligent systems to beat competitors who may do additional work or work less effectively on improving outcomes.

The world model at the center of efficient thought is an abstraction. No intelligent system need have all of its knowledge packaged and labeled *World Model* for the abstraction to pertain. *Information in memory* or *current state* are different labels we might apply to the bits that predispose an intelligent system to choose one candidate future over another when the system correctly foresees that it will prefer the former outcome to the latter one. Even if the system can't verbalize or represent such *knowledge* symbolically, intelligent behavior makes it evident. Systems can store knowledge in many different ways. Even as an abstraction, the concept of a world model helps crystallize questions such as what types of knowledge exist, how knowledge operates, and when and how experiences should modify old knowledge or produce new knowledge. The world model in efficient thought directly supports all eight functions. In short, we say the world model allows the system to anticipate what results it will experience if it executes a plan of action. Usually, this model contains ways to simulate how hypothetical states would transition into future states. In everyday affairs, for example, business people call this "what-if" analysis. The efficient thinker uses its knowledge to seek and identify plausible behaviors that it expects will yield superior results.

The efficient thinker is continually improving its world model so it can get superior results, more frequently and more reliably. Its model must make as many distinctions as needed to identify the appropriate action at each point in time. Ross Ashby labeled this the *Law of Requisite Variety*, meaning that you can't perform well in a complex environment unless you can internally distinguish differences that warrant different responses[13]. If your model doesn't distinguish red from green, for example, you can't rely on color to tell if a traffic signal says to go or to stop. 10% of adult men can't make this distinction, but they can still safely drive. How? They learn to make a different distinction and rely on that. Specifically, in vertical signals, red is at the top. But the distinctions the model makes go beyond stimulus categories to include distinctions between significant states and among alternative outputs. For example, in learning to drive legally at night, we must distinguish between drivers' licenses with no restrictions and various restricted categories of licenses, with different implied constraints. We must note the type of license we have, and our mental system accordingly must incorporate a corresponding distinction. As an example of response distinctions, we must learn differences of several sorts, including: the difference between *safe* and *unsafe levels of physical force* applied in human interactions; the difference between *acceptable* and *unacceptable levels*; and how these categories specialize further depending on *the object* of our force, making appropriate distinctions for babies, horses, spouses, dance partners, opposing football players, and co-workers. Our world model incorporates these distinctions, over time, because society requires us to employ very different levels of force in these different contexts.

So our world model makes distinctions that let us anticipate how our behaviors will produce effects and the likelihood of those effects leading to success or failure relative to our objectives. We need to use our models for multiple functions, including for the following important purposes:

- Determining what people are trying to communicate to us

- Choosing what we should be trying to achieve

- Conceiving how we might try to achieve an objective

- Estimating what we'd gain from a potential plan and what it would cost

- Deciding how we'd need to communicate and implement a chosen plan

- Determining how we'd know if a plan was failing quickly enough to try to salvage it

In addition, every use of our world model leads to inferences that may prove helpful or hurtful, confirmed or repudiated. When we experience a success or failure, we need to focus on understanding how that occurred and identifying the knowledge and inferences responsible. Based on the type of feedback received and our analysis of the responsible chain of reasoning, we can decide how to strengthen or weaken, specialize or generalize, debug or throw away the implicated knowledge in our current model. The efficient thinker is a special kind of intelligent system, using the world model for all these purposes and, at the same time, devoting considerable resources to improving the model's content, its knowledge, based on experience. Knowledge is power, and the efficient thinker continually works on expanding, improving, strengthening, and sharpening its power source.

Intelligent Control

As you know, the term *control* means many things, especially the process a system uses to adapt its behavior to optimize outcomes. In this book, we'll use the term *intelligent control* to focus on how a system chooses which, of the many reasonable things it might do, it actually should do next. Over many years, Barbara Hayes-Roth, my wife, and I have explained in a few key papers how systems perform intelligent control[14-17]. These papers show how busy systems need to work at two levels simultaneously, sometimes called the *object level* and the *meta-level*. At the object level, intelligent systems develop excellent plans for accomplishing their goals. At the *meta-level*, intelligent systems cleverly reason about which things they should think about first. If life is simple, or we are simple, or we simply don't have many resources or many options, we can consider all of our options thoroughly before acting. The calculator doesn't need intelligent control, because it has plenty of computing power to do the one thing each input key press signifies. An efficient thinker in a complex environment, however, receives inputs continually and can choose to work on any of the eight efficient thought processes at each moment in time. Meanwhile, the system continuously interacts with the environment, executing previously decided actions. Processing inputs, executing plans, planning for the future, and other worthy tasks all consume time, attention and other resources. What's an ambitious, resource-limited system to do?

We name the process used to answer that question *intelligent control*. If the system can only think about one thing at a time, it had better choose that thing wisely. At each moment, the intelligent controller needs to reassess the situation, judge whether the system should continue pursuing its current direction or should promptly reorient to begin working on a different task or pursuing a different objective. Fortunately, most complex systems can actually perform several things concurrently. Unfortunately, the possible activities for pursuing one's objectives nearly always require vastly more resources than available. Moreover, each tentative decision to do anything requires additional thinking about how to meld that action into ongoing activities without one clobbering the other. So, not only must intelligent control think about what thoughts to think first, it must also plan how to blend newly planned actions with on-going compatible actions and how to clear the way by terminating incompatible actions in ways that don't invalidate any conditions the new actions or the ongoing ones require. Maddeningly complicated, isn't it?

We can't really achieve high levels of intelligent function in complex environments without intelligent control that operates at the meta-level, reasoning about what we should focus on, how we ought to reason, and how we ought to implement actions we think we want to implement. Reasoning at the meta-level raises some potential concerns. The first is somewhat abstract. Having backed up from the object or first level to the meta- or second level, so we could reason about how we ought to reason at the first level, does this mean that we now need to back up to a meta-meta-level and from there onward to an infinite regress? I wish there were a simple and compelling answer to this question, though I've never found one. We have three choices, all of which work in practice, although none seems fully satisfactory from the standpoint of logical elegance. One alternative is the one we've described, involving just two levels. We require any and all reasoning above the first level to operate within the one and only meta-level. Another alternative requires reasoning to occupy the next higher level above the highest level it addresses. The last alternative views all reasoning as of the same most general sort, so requires all reasoning to operate at the first (and only) level, regardless of the number of embedded levels of concern. As I said, in practice we can build systems that work in any of the three ways. I prefer the two-level system because it makes clear a really big distinction. Intelligent control involves reasoning at the meta-level and influences what reasoning occurs in the efficient thinker and how quickly it occurs. In our experiments with people and computerized systems, this two-level model provides helpful distinctions that work as well as we seem to require. So with two levels, we seem to satisfy Ashby's requirement for requisite variety, as it were.

Human organizations employ an *agenda* to determine what things the organization works on and which ones get attention first. This effectively channels the behavior of the organization, assuring that the highest priority items get whatever resources can afford to provide them. Items further down the agenda get whatever resources remain after the higher priority allocations. This explains the common notion, "The person who controls the agenda, controls the outcome." Intelligent control serves just this purpose for its host system. It controls the outcome indirectly by determining which thoughts, processes, and actions should get the attention and resources needed to enact them. How does it *know* what to do? Some of intelligent control is hardwired in naturally selected systems. Humans, for example, give prompt attention to pain and immediately withdraw a limb from pain induced by intense heat.

Reordering the agenda in this way seems wired in at a low level, to insure survival. The psychologist Abraham Maslow described a hierarchy of needs whose relevance to this question seems apt[18]. Maslow said that people pursue objectives at increasingly higher levels of value or purpose, once needs at lower levels such as food, water, and shelter have been assured. Given that sustained existence depends on consuming basic necessities, any intelligent control that prevented attainment of these would induce mortal danger. Similarly, in complex environments where the being has to compete with intelligent adversaries, the intelligent controller has to assure that all available resources are applied to more strategic objectives, those that improve competitiveness, and make the being a more cunning and skilled competitor. Interestingly, a number of spiritualists and social scientists suggest that the highest objective a human can attain is one of self-absorption, where concerns with the external environment end, and where all rewards emanate from self-satisfaction. Perhaps they're right, but it's difficult to see how such people will outlast cunning and skilled competitors who have different intentions, including control of the environment and consumption of the bulk of the available resources.

In short, we compete in complex environments open to wide ranges of behaviors and control strategies. Intelligent control aims to allocate limited resources among competing demands in ways that assure we spend enough time thinking about the most important things to do, enough time actually thinking, and enough time actually doing the right things to keep us alive and comfortable in the face of competitors. The intelligent controller worries about all important limited resources, not just time. It has to allocate all critical resources prudently.

Humans and Machines as Partners

Since the dawn of history, people have invented tools to amplify human capabilities. Spears reached beyond knives, and arrows launched from bows reached even further. The industrial revolution harnessed steam and water power sources to manufacturing machines enabling teams of people and machines to reach unprecedented levels of productivity. The rise of electronics and ultimately integrated circuits produced the information revolution, where bits supplanted molecules as the principal focus of technological advance. Steady progress on automation, control systems, machine vision, robotics, expert systems, and knowledge-based problem-solving has enabled machines with advanced information-processing capabilities to perform many tasks that previously required humans. In the future, we can confidently predict that as the intelligence and other capabilities of machines steadily progress, businesses and governments will field teams of human and machine partners that possess ever increasing levels of combined capability.

J.C.R. Licklider, a former director of the information processing techniques office at DARPA, was the first to envision, describe, and directly create technology aimed at achieving the symbiosis of human and computer skill[19, 20]. His story is worth a book itself, and there is a good one by Mitch Waldrop, *The Dream Machine*.[21]

In these human-machine partnerships, each type of player has comparative advantages. Machines are tireless and relatively predictable, easily reprogrammable, and quickly reproducible or, just as quickly, terminated. Machines do well with unambiguous information written in formalized syntax with agreed upon semantics. Humans have none of these properties. In contrast, humans like variety, operate reasonably with incomplete, inconsistent, ambiguous and naturalistic communication. They sense the world across many dimensions, perceive aspects they find interesting, and convey these to others in descriptive words that are imprecise and ambiguous. They grasp human concerns and spontaneously focus resources on aspects of complex situations that they judge critical. They are judgmental. They get frustrated by excessively demanding challenges. They are emotional. They like praise, and they sting from rebukes. When they get angry, they think hard about getting even.

Given these two very different profiles, one has to question the implicit assumption that humans and machines make good partners. It's not their natural affinity that makes this partnership inevitable, though. It's their natural complementarity. People need machines to process the huge amounts of information available in a timely way. People would simply drown from this deluge. On the other hand, machines don't have much understanding of human values, the significance of events, or the intuition to choose where to focus efforts in a limitless sea of opportunities. Competitive organizations that combine and intelligently control these diverse components will achieve enormous advantages over either all-human or totally mechanized systems.

In order to combine capabilities, humans and machines will need to coordinate activities. They will need to accept tasks and report results that can inform the intelligent controller, so the agenda continually reflects results and current priorities. Based on the agenda, the intelligent controller continually assures that all processors are working on the highest-valued tasks. This means that both humans and machines have to inform and take directives from meta-level control. Specifically, the intelligent controller will need ways to ask a human to perform one task and a machine to perform another. For example, in determining how many large sized, black colored, T-shirts with pockets should be produced this week, a clothing manufacturer's intelligent controller might want to ask a human to estimate the retail climate for black T-shirts with pockets in several representative regions. The controller might ask a machine to compute estimated orders and returns of black T-shirts using a seasonally-adjusted regression model with six degrees of freedom. The intelligent controller would ask these two for their inputs as a result of (1) noting that production schedules for this item must be determined within 24 hours to avoid late deliveries and (2) determining that combinations of quantitative and qualitative estimates give optimal production targets that rarely overshoot actual sales by significant quantities.

The preceding example helps reveal the essential elements of the modern human-machine organization. These organizations must perform many important tasks, against deadlines, producing potentially significant gains or losses. Based on experience, the organization's intelligent controller learns some effective processes for determining answers to key questions that enable the organization to adapt behavior in light of improved estimates quickly enough to avoid penalties. Some of these tasks play to the strength of machines to process well defined information according to well understood algorithms or procedures. Other tasks need human judgment, intuition, or qualitative reasoning. Both types of participants will interact through work products, taking on tasks within processes, and producing intermediate results that can be handed to other processors for additional work. In the intelligent information-processing system, everybody's trying to add value to bits by improving the expected productivity of the consumers of those bits. All parties who are part of an efficient thought system cooperate to create, refine, and share world model bits so they and others can conjecture, evaluate, select, communicate, implement and control alternative planned actions. The mix of people and machine reflects the current state of technology and comparative advantages. This mix exists to think efficiently, to perform effectively, and thus to prosper in the environment.

Humans and machines cooperate and blend together in implementing the intelligent organization's world model. While some purely automated systems utilize only computerized models, most organizations employ both human experts and computer programs for modeling. The US NOAA, which monitors and forecasts weather, for example, employs dozens of computerized modeling tools in conjunction with hundreds of human meteorologists. In this teamwork, silicon-based and carbon-based memory and computation processors look at the incoming data, infer current conditions and significant components of the weather systems at work, and then project likely future states. The computer programs create forecasts at fine-grain levels, using cellular models to predict how local patterns affect nearby cells. The human reasoners consider the computer forecasts and superpose higher levels of interpretation, identifying convective super-cells, fronts, pressure ridges, and other macroscopic phenomena. Ultimately, the humans translate these higher-level interpretations into graphic and textual forecasts and warnings widely broadcast to concerned parties. Human airplane pilots, for example, listen to updated broadcasts of these weather warnings in English on designated radio frequencies as they fly. When, for example, they learn of significant convective weather in their path, they divert around it to avoid great risks to their aircraft and passengers.

A world model, thus, is recognizable by what it does, not what package it comes in. Like the old saw, "If it walks like a duck and quacks like a duck, it probably is a duck," we can identify a world model by the questions it answers, the processes it supports, and the way organizations use it. In efficient thinking, intelligent systems need a world model to assess situations, identify worthy goals and conjecture plausible plans to achieve them, to evaluate the likely consequences of possible plans, and to focus attention on important things to monitor during the plan's execution. Every organization supports these functions to some degree, using some more or less formal structures, with more or less sophisticated computational apparatus. Many organizations in the last few years have focused efforts on *knowledge management* systems, mechanisms intended to get expertise delivered wherever and whenever others need it. A world model is a particular type of knowledge base that every organization needs for efficient thought, and it should be the central focus of knowledge management efforts. Usually, however, knowledge management activities are too broad and too diffuse, lacking a detailed architecture for efficient thought, and struggling simultaneously with too many objectives to succeed.

In short, people and machines make an odd couple, one side all humorless discipline and the other side ambiguity tolerant, fuzzy, and intuitive. Because machine productivity is soaring, the ideal balance in our human-machine teams changes frequently. Effective organizations must seek continually to assess, hone, and better exploit human comparative advantages. At the same time, they must find ways to leverage those talents to ever greater extents through expanding powers of automated intelligent components. Hybrid intelligence is the winning formula.

Distribution, Telecommunication, and Coordination

Any real system occupies space, so distance separates its parts. In itty bitty systems like insects, the parts exist really close together. In great big systems like the solar system, parts orbit millions of miles apart. Distance affects how well the parts of a system can work together, because some information must flow between the parts to convey requests, communicate results, or synchronize actions. No known system can transmit information faster than the speed of light, so big distances require considerable time. The speed of light also directly affects latency in electronic circuits, so distance-induced delays constrain even our littlest machines. Biological systems, such as humans, have thinking rates and adaptive cycle times limited by how fast signals can propagate along the nerve cells' axons, transmit chemicals across synapses, and adapt membrane permeability to trigger additional cell firings. When two identical systems differ only in size, longer distances between components usually implies bigger systems act more slowly.

All intelligent systems embody an architecture of components, distributed in space, communicating over some distance, and working together to achieve objectives that no single component could accomplish by itself. In large human organizations, the components include individual employees, machines, departments, IT systems, suppliers, and so forth. Each component, viewed as a unitary entity, must communicate over distances to others and must receive and process messages from others. Every organization hopes it will avoid incurring significant losses arising from transmission or processing delays. In today's world, designers of information systems must insure important information gets to people in a timely way and in a form they find easy to consume.

Obviously, if we had a better idea about to arrange components and structure their interactions, we could in principle take all the components in a system and rearrange them, laying out a new architecture. Benefits we might attain this way could include faster, better, and cheaper performance of the system's principal functions. We might, on the other hand, discover that the new architecture detrimentally affected performance, mostly likely as a result of worsened communication. By increasing distances between some components, we would have increased the latency of messages. We might also introduce communication barriers, such as changes in required languages for business communications, as would occur if we moved some operations from North America to France. We could make coordination more difficult, by increasing cultural barriers, inflicting inconsistent regulations or standards on different parts of the organization, or making synchronization meetings difficult, as when people work business hours on different continents. How well we lay out the organization and stitch its parts together determines how well it can compete and perform.

The principal techniques for stitching distributed organizations together are business processes, telecommunications, and collaboration. Business process management (BPM) methods and tools enable organizations to specify how routine work should be performed[22, 23]. To illustrate, a company might describe using a BPM toolkit how to accept and fulfill orders for its products. The process would describe ways orders should enter the company, which IT system would record them, which procedures would check order soundness, steps needed to validate the purchaser's credit worthiness, and additional tasks to move the product to the customer. Process managers select departments or outside organizations to perform each process, task, or step based on the capabilities and qualifications demanded by the process specifications. These BPM specifications resemble a computer program dictating how the overall organization should accomplish the objective of "accept and fulfill an order." The BPM system helps the organization execute this "program," through combining tasks performed both by humans and machines. BPM depends on an explicit description of what each component should do, in what order, with what inputs, and producing what outputs. Business rules and other logical means can reduce the need for managers to work out all details in advance, leaving computer problem-solvers to optimize assignments and allocations in real-time that reflect the current agenda and resources available. In any case, business processes define how the components of an organization collaborate, constituting ad hoc systems that individually accomplish each vital function.

For a physically distributed organization, process specifications define the organization's procedures abstractly, leaving open the final resolution of many details. In particular, they often implicitly treat communication as a negligible, free, essentially instantaneous and, hence, ignorable task. However, we don't possess small, compact machines that can perform these processes. Most real organizations find it necessary to distribute their performers and resources widely in space. For example, they often try to organize centers of activity with sufficient volumes of work to maintain a sustainable size or "critical mass." Often organizations site these centers where they can obtain the most valued resources required for the center's key activity. This leads to many competing organizations often choosing the same locale for centers of a particular type. Skilled workers and suppliers who support that type of activity then also gravitate to the same area.

As a result of widespread physical distribution of capabilities, organizations rely on communication to stitch its components together, inducing delays, and creating opportunities for a wide variety of failures. Distributed organizations have co-evolved with the telecommunications industry. As communication capabilities improved, organizations exploited them, distributed further, and aspired for more. They seek ways the components can coordinate, work quickly and effectively, and synchronize as required, although separated by ever-increasing distances. Communication technologies support these requirements by supplying a hierarchy of services, layered like a wedding cake. At the lowest level, telecommunications provides physical connectivity between communicating entities so electronic signals can jump the gap. If they can't signal each other somehow, two parties can't communicate bits of information. At higher levels, telecommunications provide ways to set up and maintain links or *connections* that enable two partners to start up and conduct a *conversation*. This allows lots of bits to be exchanged with a minimum of overhead, and it also allows lots of multiplexed conversations to share common physical communication resources. At the highest levels, telecommunications systems aim to convey important task-relevant information quickly, reliably, and in ways that minimize processing costs. These goals usually mean that evolved organizations employ concise codes for their tasks and special communication processing subsystems that don't require senders and receivers to interrupt their other activities for routine task-related communications.

Collaboration methods enable multiple components to work together on a common goal [11, 24, 25]. These too span many levels from simple coordination techniques to sophisticated problem-solving methodologies. When an aircraft pilot taxis a plane up to the airport gate, the ground crew-person uses hand signals to indicate when the pilot should change direction, how much, and for how long. The two work together toward a common goal, namely getting the plane to the right location adjacent to the gate. The collaboration language employs a set of shared hand signals, standardized by the FAA. Continuing up the levels within air travel, for example, the pilot and co-pilot collaborate in the control of the aircraft, usually dividing a set of tasks between them so more work can be done by intelligent processors in a fixed amount of time. The pilot collaborates with route planners and with weather service personnel to determine both initial routes and dynamically revised routes when necessary. The pilot collaborates with air traffic controllers to determine precise headings, altitudes, radio channels, departure and arrival procedures. Air traffic controllers collaborate with others at their same site to divide and conquer the local traffic challenges. They also collaborate with other controllers responsible for adjacent regions to hand off aircraft leaving one area and entering a neighboring one. Pilots collaborate with other pilots to communicate important reports about enroute significant events, such as icing or turbulence. Pilots may need to convey such reports through flight service personnel, who receive and transmit enroute weather information among pilots. The air control system shows many routine types of collaboration to get its basic function accomplished: moving airframes around and above the surface of the earth, consistent with expectations of the shippers and passengers who pay for them.

All sizable systems are distributed, and this creates a challenge for the components: how should they work together to achieve objectives? The answer requires that they divide work into tasks and coordinate task executions. Being distant from one another, the components must communicate effectively to accomplish the needed coordination. When desired behavior requires that one party possesses information that another currently holds, they need to communicate. The requirements for effective communication include the following:

1. The communicating parties must choose signals and agree on their meaning.

2. Senders must transport sufficient signals to appropriate recipients.

3. Recipients must receive, digest, and understand signals quickly enough to modify their states appropriately.

4. Recipients must initiate appropriate responses before the received information becomes stale.

Only with sufficient timely information, communicated from afar, can each component play a supporting part in the overall coordinated processes the organization requires to achieve its objectives. The dumber the components, the more dependent they are on being told what to do, at every step of the process. The busier the components, the less they can afford to spend processing insignificant messages. Obviously, all distributed organizations can benefit by optimizing how they communicate.

Distributed Intelligent Organizations

Intelligent organizations are nearly always distributed too, but they can do more with less than dumber ones. Previously, when we defined intelligent systems, we focused on their ability to use knowledge to innovate to adapt successfully. We also pointed out that intelligent control must address the meta-level questions of what to work on, what to think about, and how to allocate limited resources. We thus far ignored, however, how intelligent systems need to communicate. In addition to the capabilities thus far ascribed to intelligence, we find that distributed intelligent systems use knowledge to increase the productivity of communication. Simply stated, the distributed intelligent organization uses its knowledge to minimize the costs of required communication. As we have said before, communication requirements arise from a need to coordinate the components of divided and physically distributed organization. When components need information from afar to perform excellently, that information constitutes a communication requirement. Intelligent organizations use their knowledge to find ways to obviate communication or significantly reduce it. Smart organizations do more with fewer bits and do it faster.

We've already seen some of the tricks that make communication more efficient in intelligent organizations, illustrated throughout the previous paragraphs. The discussion of how communications occur in the air traffic control system illustrated many of these. Here's a list of 17 smartest things organizations do to use their knowledge to achieve better coordination with less communication:

1. Define a standardized set of unambiguous, concise, semantically important messages.

2. Require all components to use the standard messages.

3. Train components to use the messages correctly and assure that they do.

4. Communicate only to those who need to know.

5. Don't communicate things that aren't needed by the recipient.

6. Only communicate things that the recipient can processed and exploit in the time available.

7. If there's too much to communicate, convey the most vital things first.

8. Use communication modalities and channels that don't interrupt other resource-limited processes.

9. Don't communicate or repeat things already understood.

10. Don't communicate information about small, insignificant changes.

11. Estimate the impact your information will have for the recipient, and use that estimate to prioritize communications.

12. Anticipate how the behavior of the recipient would vary in response to the receiving your information.

13. Assume the recipient of your information most likely will behave as you anticipate.

14. Assume no received information means "no news," because your correspondents would let you know otherwise.

15. Check your assumptions from time to time.

16. Estimate how often it's worth checking assumptions.

17. Assure that others in your organization operate by the same assumptions you do.

These 17 communication design ideas show how a distributed intelligent system can use knowledge to make communication more effective, getting more bang for the bit. Let's make sure the air traffic system illustration is easy to map onto each of these ideas. That's what we'll do now.

The ground crew's hand signals to the pilot illustrate idea 1. In fact, the entire air traffic system employs precisely defined terms and fixed communication messages. Point 2 is accomplished by federal regulations and conveyed through instructors and tested through examiners. Only those who know the system can earn licenses, and they can lose their licensing by failing to adhere to the conventions. Ideas 4 through 7 characterize communications between controllers and pilots. Extraneous conversation occurs only in quiet times and then just as a pleasantry. Pilots receive many important kinds of data outside their auditory channel that is reserved mostly for dialog with controllers. For example, situational weather, traffic, and radar data reach the pilot via the aircraft's graphical displays, so the pilot can use other channels to take them in as soon as possible. This illustrates point 8. Ideas 9 and 10 are illustrated by the fact that controllers don't tell pilots more than once what heading or altitude they should fly, unless the pilot fails to acknowledge or comply. Pilots don't report small deviations in heading, altitude or speed, but significant deltas must be reported. The amount of a deviation that is significant has been determined by the FAA, because it would have a good chance of leading to an unanticipated conflict in the traffic system. Ideas 11-13 are exemplified by communications from a controller to a pilot to execute an emergency course change to avoid a potential collision. The controller tells the pilot where the conflicting traffic is, what its apparent heading is, and sometimes which avoidance maneuver to execute. Everyone expects this will have the desired result. Idea 14 allows pilots to continue on their plans and routes without constantly reconfirming. No information is no news. Of course, it could be that one's radio has gone kaput, so the pilot checks that assumption, as in idea 15, either by listening to other transmissions or by periodically checking with ATC to reconfirm the health of the radios. The pilot develops through experience familiarity with patterns of silence that allow him or her to have a good sense of how long is too long. This illustrates idea 16. Fortunately for all participants in air traffic, the FAA in the US (and other bodies in other jurisdictions) mandate that all components learn and abide by the same communication rules. This means the system as a whole spends a minimum of resources on communicating what's required to coordinate overall effective and safe behavior.

Most organizations perform a wider variety of functions than the air traffic control system, and most have not achieved comparable proficiency at communication. In fact, most organizations develop communication cultures around the technologies they have available when they mature. Companies such as Hewlett-Packard matured when their best technology was voice mail, and the senior HP personnel still rely on voicemail for much of their critical communication. Another company, in the same industry, such as Compaq, grew up with email as their preferred technology. When HP bought Compaq, these two cultures collided and a new hybrid struggled with how best to communicate. Military organizations often have communication technologies that lag those in business, because they have longer acquisition cycles and greater security concerns. As a result, many military organizations attain low levels of intelligent efficacy in their communication practices.

The 17 design ideas for intelligent communication provide a practical checklist for organizations. Most organizations have a long way to go to approach an optimum level of intelligent communication. Because time and effort spent communicating necessarily comes out of the same resources available for thinking and acting, the quality of communication often limits the quality of the overall results an organization can achieve. Superb competitors communicate intelligently. Diffuse communicators achieve lackluster results. Fortunately, there are some simple ways to put systems together out of components that combine to work intelligently. Thus, we now turn to architecture.

The Architecture of Distributed Intelligence

Given that there's always "more than one way to skin a cat," we can always find many ways to design organizations for skinning cats or for any other purpose. Nevertheless, one really good approach to designing distributed intelligent systems has emerged. The overall approach it provides we refer to as *architecture*. The term architecture has many different meanings, but the one we intend here follows: a basic scheme for combining components so they can accomplish the overall design objectives in efficient and effective ways. To describe the architecture, we need to identify what kinds of components will be employed and how they communicate. The components, of course, perform functions by consuming resources, accepting inputs, computing what state changes and outputs to make, and then producing outputs and making the identified state changes. In addition, as we've seen, all intelligent distributed systems need to spend effort to determine the best things to do and the best messages to communicate. The architecture we describe provides answers to all of these questions.

The architecture is illustrated in Fig. 5. We term the architecture *fractal*, because that term has been widely applied to structures that are self-similar when viewed at different scales, as when one zooms in or out to vary the level of detail. Granite mountains present fractal profiles: as you zoom in with a telephoto lens on smaller and smaller parts of the profile, the silhouette looks identical, because granite slopes are craggy, and the crags and slopes repeat in similar ways at each smaller scale. In a similar way, the fractal architecture repeats, because each system comprises components that are themselves subsystems made up of components, and this hierarchy of subsystem levels

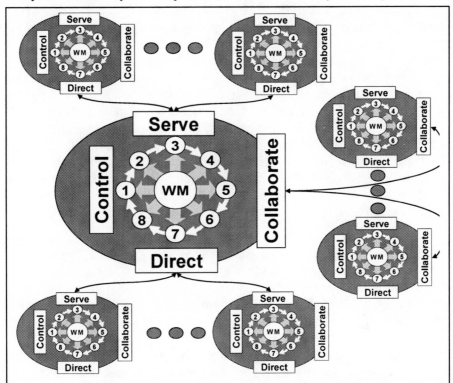

Figure 5. Fractal distributed intelligent systems.

Complex intelligent systems should utilize a fractal architecture as in holarchic organizations. Very large-scale, dynamic, adaptive organizations benefit by using standard frameworks that relate all components to one another through standardized interfaces. By embedding efficient thought in every component, enabling each component to communicate and interact with others based on standardized protocols, and coordinating and controlling resources intelligently, these organizations achieve scale, power, efficiency and competitive success.

continues recursively. Of course, all real systems ultimately bottom out at "atomic" or indivisible components. For some analytical purposes, we might also choose to ignore internal details and view some composite components as atomic. The fractal structure aids analysis and simplifies management in part because of this capacity for allowing one to suppress details below one's current level of concern. In many real organizations, the lowest, or most disaggregated level, of components managers consider usually corresponds to a single person or a department. In military fighting organizations, the lowest level might correspond to a platoon or perhaps an individual soldier. This recursive, self-similar structure is also called holarchic, after Koestler, who coined the term [1]. He was strongly motivated to identify the membrane that determined the difference between *inside* a system and *outside* a system. He found that organizational behavior often reflects competing motives and influences on different sides of that boundary. Further, he explained many pathologies of individual and group behavior as symptoms of unhealthy imbalances between these concurrent internal and external activities. We won't pursue these psychological theories further, focusing instead on how to exploit new technologies and methods to develop and sustain extremely capable organizations.

With fractal systems, we only need to understand how one component works to comprehend the whole system. That makes our task much easier. The fractal architecture has an additional, related, major benefit. When people want to construct a component, at any level, for any function, they can use the same principles of construction. This means that people in widely differing contexts can use identical methods and tools to build intelligent components that can combine to create distributed intelligent systems. Nature itself appears to have seized these benefits in the development of intelligent biological systems, and several engineering groups have repeatedly employed the same principles in designing human-machine intelligent systems.

The figure depicts the archetypical component as the large central oval. The component presents three interfaces to external components. One interface receives service requests, one directs others to provide services, and another one enables collaboration. Internal to each component we see a world model, the eight process steps of efficient thought, and a control function. A given component can contain other components within it, each of which has a similar structure, but the figure doesn't depict these explicitly. The figure also doesn't show internal communications, but they serve the save purpose as the external ones: direct others to serve, serve others, or collaborate with others.

We'll now explain the basic communications to clarify how the components work together to accomplish objectives.

Illustrative uses of the fractal architecture include creating a single machine, such as a programmable robot, a commercial organization such as a print shop, or a military organization such as an armored battalion. We could have picked higher or lower levels of aggregation, with no loss of relevance or accuracy. For example, we might have said a machine shop as opposed to a robot, an accounting department inside the print shop, or a Joint Task Force rather than just a component battalion. For simplicity, we'll take the print shop as the focal example.

The print shop exists, like most businesses, to take orders and covert them into profit. To accomplish this mission, the shop must translate the orders into process steps, then provide needed resources to the processes and execute them, deliver the work products to the customers and invoice them, collect and deposit their payments, and pay the suppliers' bills. Lastly, over the long run, collections must exceed payments.

When viewed as a fractal organization, the print shop accomplishes things by communicating essential messages to appropriate components. Let's now consider how communications work in the fractal architecture, using the print shop to illustrate:

Through the Serve interface: Customers or superiors make requests or give commands for service. They describe an objective, specify a task, or identify a process they want performed. They also convey success criteria, acceptable end states, or other stopping conditions. The serving component accepts these communications and agrees to perform the desired service. The serving component conveys the finished result and reports on its work, especially reporting such states as successful completion or failure. Many applications explicitly communicate about *hypothetical* commands and expected costs, because these enable the serve interface to receive requests for bids and to respond by making proposals, including prices, for work that the requestor might subsequently order. In the print shop, the customer might ask for a bid for 100 customized holiday greeting cards, and the print shop might reply with a bid for $150. The customer might then place the order. The print shop might then report an expected completion and pick-up time. The print shop would then focus internally on converting the order into actions.

Through the Direct interface: Customers or superiors issue commands or make requests by emitting these through Direct interfaces. In response, they receive through these interfaces bids, reports, and results. When they receive unacceptable bids, results or reports, they must deal with the *exception*, the violated expectation. They may make service requests to multiple competing suppliers, and they may iterate on the specification until they get a bid they find acceptable. At that point they issue an order and can expect performance results consistent with those represented by the service provider during the bidding process. In the print shop example the customer conveys through its Direct interface a request for a bid and an order for the customized holiday cards. The customer receives back through its Direct interface a bid, an order confirmation with expected completion date, and the finished holiday cards. Within the print shop, the management determines what components should produce the bid, the expected completion date, and the customized cards. The management conveys corresponding directives to the appropriate components through its Direct interface. The components that receive these directives may, in turn, divide the corresponding tasks into pieces and pass associated requests to lower-level, subordinate components.

Through the Collaborate interface: Components can have many reasons to collaborate with other components. They are frequently motivated to share world model information. They also regularly seek to divide and conquer tasks in clever ways so they can attain better results or consume few resources. Every component must perform the eight process steps in efficient reasoning. It must devise good plans to accomplish tasks on its agenda. Often the best plans dictate that components should only do tasks they excel at and should collaborate with others to accomplish tasks they do better. In the context our example, the print shop may work with a computerized page layout consultant to do graphic design. It may also use an outside accounting firm to do its bookkeeping and invoicing. Collaborators may employ a broad and diverse set of messages, but their communication focuses on three principal functions: (1) aligning state information in their world models; (2) decomposing overall tasks to enable the assignment of subtasks to partners and the coordination of their constituent activities; and (3) improving outcomes or reducing costs by appropriately exploiting the partners' distinct advantages.

Control: The control element of each component schedules activities and allocates the resources needed to perform them. In low-level components, such as a printing press, the controller might sequence paper flow and regulate ink flow, start and stop batches, and make the machine ready for changeovers between jobs. At a higher level, the control unit determines which orders to process next and assures that resource exhaustion doesn't bring planned processes to a sudden halt. Control can participate in pricing, to raise bid prices when demand exceeds available, for example. At this high level, experienced personnel usually perform the control function. Operations managers in the print shop, for example, use their knowledge to balance capacity and demand and to adjust pricing with the goal of maximizing profit.

At each level of the print shop, control aims to accomplish the highest valued tasks with the most efficient possible utilization of resources. To do this job well, the control element must estimate the costs and benefits of performing different possible actions. It must place deferred activities on an agenda and perform the highest rated activities immediately. This type of intelligent control was first implemented in the Hearsay-II speech understanding system by a "focus of attention" component developed by Victor Lesser and me [16]. This component enabled the system to find plausible interpretations of spoken utterances extremely rapidly even though it might seem reasonable to consider millions of plausible alternatives. Barbara Hayes-Roth and I generalized this seminal idea in our work on meta-level reasoning in planning and control[15], and she subsequently developed a robust architecture and technology for intelligent control[14, 17]. For reasons we have already discussed, no resource-constrained entity can compete successfully in complex, dynamic environments without intelligent control.

Two organizations in the United States were first to study and apply this fractal architecture: the robotics group at NIST under James Albus and my research group at Teknowledge. Albus and his colleagues developed several architectures for hierarchical control, sometimes called NASREM and ultimately referred to as RCS [26-28]. These researchers originally pointed out many important properties of the fractal architecture. For example, in natural systems, the time scale relevant to each layer in a hierarchy increases by a factor of approximately 10 at each higher level. Thus, in the print shop, the chief executive may be thinking in terms of a 3-year strategic plan, the chief of operations may be thinking in terms of this month's and quarter's financial results, the manager of each service line is concerned with efficient utilization and production through the next 12 hours, the press operator is concerned with setting up and operating the machine during the next few minutes, and the electronic servo controls on the presses are operating on sub-second cycles.

Each level operates approximately an order of magnitude faster as we go down the hierarchy. Moreover, to do one's job well, each level needs state data whose precision corresponds to that level's time scale. The servo-controller needs real time data, with the scale of milliseconds or centiseconds, spanning the past few seconds; the machine operator observes the machine for trends over minutes; the service manager observes data over hours; the operations chief observes data over days; and the CEO observes data over months. In a related way, the precision of these data correlate with the time horizon: data over shorter horizons requires greater precision than data over longer horizons.

Extending some of the NIST ideas, my group at Teknowledge elaborated the fractal model both as a general methodology for composing intelligent systems from heterogeneous components [29-33] and also as a software framework, or domain-specific software architecture (DSSA), for distributed intelligent control and management (DICAM) applications [34-37]. As part of a DARPA program on DSSAs for intelligent control, we applied the DICAM architecture to a broad category of motorized artillery systems.

We confirmed the NIST group's findings about order of magnitude differences between adjacent levels needed for response time, data precision, and planning horizons. Some additional general observations emerged. In collaboration with Prof. Gene Franklin of Stanford, we began to understand why natural selection would favor this fractal architecture. By stratifying functional capabilities over multiple levels that differ by an order of magnitude in time constants, each serving component operates in the context of a slowly changing director. From the viewpoint of a component at any level, directives it receives change relatively slowly or infrequently.

In effect, this architecture assures that each superior provides a working context to subordinates that seems practically constant to them. This means that each component can accomplish a great deal of work, in terms of its own time constant, before it has to adapt to changing requests from above. This enables the distributed organization to achieve *stability*, to pursue results long enough to accomplish results, before participants have to change aim and redirect efforts. If changes from above arrive too frequently, the component will "thrash," practically never finishing anything. If you've ever worked in a chaotic organization, you'll recognize this all too common syndrome.

Another feature of these fractal systems is that the world model appropriate to each component reflects the level of detail and time horizon it focuses on. When components use models to plan, predict, control, and monitor activities these models must address the appropriate time scale and exhibit the precision required at that level. Thus, the world model stratifies knowledge, so each component can operate with knowledge appropriate to its level of abstraction.

Components must cooperate to share information about their world models. At each higher level, elements of the world model must aggregate or abstract data from lower levels. So, for example, the operations manager of the print shop must continually update his overall expectations to aggregate forecasts from each of his business line managers. Similarly, when components plan to accomplish some task, they adjust their world model to incorporate expected results, described in terms appropriate to each component's time horizon and level of precision. Thus, at each level, components keep in their world model data at an appropriate level of precision about past, present, and future anticipated results. Continuing our example, the operations manager maintains a good aggregated model of past results, current operations, and expected future results. The manager uses these, for example, to detect worrisome trends or to assure the total operation progresses satisfactorily toward quarterly objectives.

Let's now look at the overall print shop to reinforce the important points. The world model describes how people in the printing business think things work. The model comprises knowledge and reasoning capabilities distributed among the employees and their information systems. They use this model to generate plans, forecast results, and assess performance. The CEO, for example, knows what kinds of business results a print shop of this size should achieve in its market segment. Specifically, the CEO should have a good feel for seasonal demand, competitive prices, return on assets, utilization, and other measures of competitive performance. This enables the CEO, supported by subordinate components, to forecast business levels, cash requirements, capacity requirements, and so forth. At lower levels in the business, managers have models of how processes work, what levels of performance they can attain with different qualities and quantities of inputs, how to assure that processes stay on track, and how to change from one process to another when required. This kind of knowledge about the printing business enables each component to forecast is own performance and costs accurately. This ability, in turn, enables the component to provide bids for its services in response to requests from above. Getting these bids right is important, because components that don't keep their promises don't keep getting business. When components break their promises, customers move their business to a competing component or fire the responsible manager.

Each of the communications that occur between components should be designed in accordance with the 17 design rules given in the previous section. In fact, the fractal architecture makes this easier to accomplish, because it stereotypes most of the conversations. For example, when requesting bids for services, components should use standardized forms to describe their requirements. Similarly, components bidding for work should adopt routine templates for the bid information. Within an organization, this is easy to do, because the organization can impose standardized communication on its components. Between components in different organizations, no single party can mandate adoption of any particular standard, although in principle everyone benefits from improved communication. Given the potential benefits, several electronic marketplaces and industry-specific exchanges have adopted standard document definitions for bids and orders. Companies with relatively high skills in IT in a number of industry areas have promoted the development of industry-specific standards for e-commerce. Well managed supply chains, often containing dozens of independent autonomous companies, have fully automated every type of communication required to accomplish scheduling, production, delivery, and invoicing.

The fractal model provides a universally applicable architecture for distributed intelligent systems. It lays out the generic role of components, describes what functions each component must do for itself, specifies how components relate to one another, and characterizes the role of communications within and between components. The model also shows organizations how to optimize its results through use of intelligent communication and control. Table 1 lists the 12 principal features of the fractal architecture. In the second column, the table concisely describes how the organization benefits from each feature. In the next column, the table illustrates how that feature operates in the print shop example. In the last column, the table describes the risks an organization would face if it didn't exploit that feature. That column conveys what it potentially costs to eliminate a feature. Taken together, the table reveals why high performing organizations need each aspect of the fractal architecture and how each one produces key benefits. In short, the table implies that the fractal model is *necessary* and *sufficient* for the organization to obtain the benefits described. In science generally, we consider as essential theorized properties that prove both necessary and sufficient.

Table 1. Principal Features of the Fractal Architecture and its Benefits.

Feature	Benefit	Print Shop Examples	Risks Incurred if Eliminated
1) **Hierarchy**	Maximizes behavioral variety resulting from a fixed number of components each operating in a policy context provided to it by a superior	CEO chooses markets, products, and services; managers acquire equipment and establish processes; staff operate equipment and transform material	Each component has to consider all issues and all data to establish a context for its own actions, resulting in costly repetition and risking uncoordinated activity stemming from incompatible assumptions
2) **Self-Similarity**	Organizations can be designed for any range of variety using identical methods and supporting tools	Each level can manage subordinates by setting objectives, getting timely reports, and focusing on exceptions	Every pair of interacting components needs to develop and validate a unique means of achieving effective coordination
3) **10X Differences Between Levels in Time-Scale and Precision**	Stability achieved by changing context for lower levels at a rate they find slow; exponential range (10^N) of	Each employee is busy, all day, processing information at different levels of abstraction. Changes in plans at any level needn't flow down urgently	Plan changes in one component might need to be communicated quickly to interacting components, causing these to interrupt their

	behavioral variety spanned by N levels; levels process information at equal rates assuring no bottlenecks arise	to levels below, allowing the lower levels to continue performing smoothly for some time	work and produce a herky-jerky behavior. Each component would have to process more raw data to extract relevant information. Data gluts would overwhelm top levels.
4) Task Decomposition	High-level objectives attained by assembling sub-objectives' results. Components evolve processes that produce results reliably. Specialization leads to higher performance and greater efficiency.	Shop breaks "Satisfy Customer" process into process steps: requirements elucidation; bidding; order entry; production; delivery; invoicing; collection. In turn, define processes for each step. Particular company components take responsibility for each process.	Without decomposition, each customer's order would require one component to perform all tasks. This would stifle specialization. Each component would aim to perform all tasks well enough. No component would excel at anything.
5) Concise Communication of Task Delegation and Reporting	Components interact with one another in few, specialized ways. They develop precise and concise ways to convey their requirements	The executive conveys business goals and budgets to managers. The managers convey processes, metrics, and schedules to service line operators. The service line operators convey	In the absence of a precise language and protocol for delegating tasks and reporting results, interactions among components would take more effort to

	and describe their results. They coordinate precisely, with a minimum of delay and wasted effort.	tasks, resources, quality metrics to individual staff. Staff controls machines.	accomplish the same result. Communication failures would increase. As a consequence, inappropriate activities and costs would increase.
6) **Standard Interfaces**	We can describe and model components in a uniform way, regardless of their purpose or level. A single set of tools can be used to integrate them or support information transfers.	Each unit can report: how its actual performance over a relevant time period compared to expected results; how discrepancies implicate faulty assumptions, decisions or execution; and how it plans to fix these problems going forward.	Every component could define its own information requirements and impose these on all others who need its services. Each component could choose to provide whatever information it wanted to others. This would reduce efficiency and retard learning.
7) **Efficient Thought**	Each component uses its knowledge to choose best available plans and learns from experience to improve its future performance.	Service line operators discover they undershoot performance goals due to poor inventory management. In response, they improve their demand forecasting and replenishment processes.	Components don't generate explicit expectations so don't know where to focus their search for causes of problems. They don't make world model assumptions explicit, so can't consciously assess and improve

			them. They don't improve.
8) Local Control	Each component knows best how to prioritize its activity to get best results when resources are constrained.	The operations manager expedites orders for important customers. The printer operator keeps all machines busy, even when the schedule planned to put all jobs serially on the same machine, leaving another one idle.	Without local intelligence prioritizing tasks in dynamic contexts, many opportunities for incremental efficiency are wasted. A 1% slow-down at every level of the organization can compound to produce significant overall losses.
9) Local World Models	Each component accesses and uses local knowledge and information appropriate to its level of responsibility and analysis, thereby reducing delays and errors.	The executive uses knowledge about the printing industry and competitive benchmarks on other companies. The machine operator checks feeds and speeds against machine norms.	Lacking an explicit world model, components don't know what information they should use, where to get it, or how to convert it into changes of behavior. They waste time processing irrelevant data.
10) Distributed Global World Model	Interacting components align their world models, by assuring	The operations manager periodically verifies that actual inventory and cash	Different components use their own models but no efforts are expended to align

	aggregated results at one level agree with abstractions used at the higher level. Discrepancies spur investigations and, ultimately, model changes.	flows correspond to the more simplified model the executive uses in his annual budgets and plans.	these and verify consistency. Anomalous results arise across the organization, but each component sees its own results as consistent with known facts.
11) Internal or External Sub-components	Functions decompose mostly hierarchically, but many processes use sub-components belonging to different organizations. Components can out-source processes to external organizations, allowing for additional efficiencies.	The print shop out-sources personnel functions to an HR Services firm, and it also out-sources accounting. It relies on a supplier to manage its raw materials logistics, and that supplier provides just-in-time deliveries of printing stock and ink.	Organizations that retain all functions internally spend more of their resources on tasks that are of secondary importance to competitiveness. Given limited resources, any shift from highest priority concerns diminishes overall competitive performance.
12) Non-hierarchical Collaboration	Components combine their knowledge to determine how to accomplish objectives in better ways	The operations manager determines that inventory management problems are reducing	Organizations with rigid hierarchical communication adapt very slowly to new conditions and often suppress

	than they could alone. Ad hoc combinations of expertise solve unprecedented problems quickly.	productivity so invites suppliers to suggest remedies. This leads to out-sourcing inventory management and JIT delivery.	internal evidence of failure. Power vests in high-level *positions* rather than in *people* with valuable knowledge. Innovation lags.

Though general and widely applicable, the fractal architecture doesn't actually do anything by itself. The architecture provides a rough blueprint for assembling good parts into a winning organization. It doesn't, however, fill out the details. Each organization needs to have the model tailored to its own competitive arena and populated with knowledge available only to specialists in that domain. Complex organizations spend decades formalizing the knowledge that supports efficient thinking and intelligent control. That knowledge becomes one of the most valuable assets of each organization. It underlies whatever information superiority that organization achieves in its own competitive environment. As knowledge accumulates and improves, performance increases, and the rich get richer.

Just as principles of accounting do not manufacture things, make profits or even accomplish bookkeeping for any actual organization, the architecture of distributed intelligent systems doesn't demonstrate superiority in any actual competitive environment. The architecture merely tells us what types of components we need, how they should relate, what functions they should demonstrate, and how we'd assure the efficiency and effectiveness of component implementations. Those contributions should prove vital in building and operating competitive organizations. Equipped with this general scheme for winning organizations, you should see quickly how to improve you own organization dramatically. Most organizations are so far from the ideal, they can quickly move to significantly improved positions. On the other hand, some organizations such as Dell, Amazon and FedEx, built with new concepts and technology, are moving fast towards the ideal. Each demonstrates a solid understanding of the advantages of the fractal distributed intelligent architecture. The architecture dictates design rules vital to the survival of every complex, distributed organization operating in modern competitive arenas.

Network-Centric Systems

Networks have been familiar structures in our environment for much of modern history. We all use transportation networks, such as highway networks and rail networks, on a daily basis. Although *we* don't travel down telephone or power networks, the electrons we employ reach their destinations that way. Computer networks have been in place for about 40 years, starting with simple proprietary networks. The computer networks evolved into sophisticated proprietary networks during the 1980s and 90s. Subsequently, proprietary networks began to give way to expansive open networks, especially the Internet. For nearly 20 years, Sun Microsystems has touted the concept that "the network is the computer." Their slogan emphasizes that all computing systems consist of storage and processing units and that owners may distribute these units in arbitrary ways so long as they tie them together with a network.

The rise of the World Wide Web (W3) over the last few years has joined with the maturing of Internet browsers and electronic commerce (e-business) to give most users of technology a palpable experience of *network-centric systems*. Network-centric systems deliver services to end-users by employing needed capabilities wherever they are on an accessible network. The way I can purchase a book from a third-party vendor on Amazon's web site provides a good illustration. When I buy a book on Amazon from a supplier listed in the "other used and new" booksellers category, I get the full *network-centric experience*. Amazon's servers provide the user interface I employ and also provide order entry and billing services. The third-party sellers update the prices they quote periodically, and their pricing systems furnish those changes to Amazon for listing on any web pages it generates that cite those sellers. When I confirm my order, Amazon transmits my order transmitted to the third-party bookseller, who in turn transmits the order and my address to its fulfillment center's computer systems. The bookseller and fulfillment service generate several other transactions to update inventory and account for the financial exchanges. Finally, the fulfillment center accesses a physical book, packages it, and orders pick up and delivery services from a package shipping company, whose systems track the package and furnish tracking information back to all the systems up the line. I receive a shipping confirmation and a tracking number from Amazon in my email, hosted on my ISP's mail server, and later I retrieve this information from the mail server on read it through my email application.

This simple and mundane example of e-business shows how the work gets done by a myriad of relatively independent components that coordinate and synchronize via network communications. Just a few years ago, every retail transaction conformed to a fixed protocol modeled on in-store transactions. Computer systems in those days aimed to get inventory to bookstore shelves so that the bookstore cashier could accept payment from a customer who would bring the chosen purchases to the register so the cashier could bag the books before the customer removed them from the store. Every bookstore worked the same way. The bookstore had a small number of local systems for cash and inventory management. The publisher and distributor had systems for selling inventory to the bookstores and accounting for volume sales, discounts, and returns. That was how bookselling had always been done.

Businesses over the last two decades began to realize that they could significantly improve profits by holding down the amount of money tied up in inventory. Unsold books on the shelf cost money to make and stock, and the store never needs more on hand than the next customer offers to buy. More expensive products, such as cars, televisions, or electronic control modules, similarly tie up a lot of capital when they sit either in finished goods inventory or in partially assembled products called work in progress (WIP). Even worse, a large stock in inventory can lose value, as when new generations of electronic products supersede previously built ones that remain unsold.

Sophisticated businesses began looking at ways they could economize, particularly by minimizing the cost of inventory. A vertically integrated company, such as one that grows timber, makes paper products, and sells paper through its own sales force, can take full responsibility for inventory management. To do this, the company determines how much finished stock it needs to meet demands without imposing unwanted delays on customers. Then the company keeps that minimal amount of inventory on hand and tries to produce additional finished goods "just in time" to satisfy future orders.

Most companies in the last two decades shifted from vertical integration to supply chain management, where each company plays a small role in any product's overall production, sale, and delivery. Companies that "manufacture" personal computers (PCs), for example, usually do little more than coordinate other companies' production and delivery, focusing mostly themselves on putting their own brand logo on the machine and its support services. These manufacturers have driven almost all cash out of the inventory problem, by synchronizing everybody else's productions and deliveries so that everything arrives just in time (JIT) for each successive process step. The retail store keeps a very small number of PCs in inventory at the retail store. In other product categories, such as refrigerators, all finished goods in the store serve exclusively as display models. When a customer purchases a refrigerator at the retail store, the store schedules a delivery for that model of refrigerator. For leading brands, deliveries originate from a regional center that maintains just enough inventory to make daily deliveries for all retailers in the region.

A recent news article lauded P&G's vision and persistence in making inventory tracking precise for a broad range of consumer products[15]:

> It sounded like a wild-eyed dot-com fantasy. But Procter & Gamble's 1999 idea to package thousands of products with tiny radio-powered computer chips is catching on, from Gillette to Wal-Mart Stores. P&G, an early investor in the technology, is leading the charge. It sees the radio-frequency ID chips ultimately tracking nearly every item it makes, from Crest to Pampers. The idea is to tie production to real-time sales at the store, cutting time and inventory out of the supply chain while keeping store shelves stocked 24/7. The first step: P&G will have radio chips on cartons and pallets of goods by 2005.

Network-centric systems access and configure resources of types required on an *as-needed basis* to deliver the product, service, or effect required with a minimum of fixed assets, overhead, and friction. The US military and its allies believe that network-centric systems are the right way to deliver military services as well. This nullifies traditional ways of fighting wars, such as moving three times as many support personnel for each warfighter into the theater before conflict begins. The emerging concepts of *network-centric systems, minimum fixed commitments*, and *JIT* mean that DoD hopes to accomplish most missions with drastically reduced numbers of resources. To achieve comparable or superior results with significantly reduced resources requires the kind of distributed intelligence considered in this chapter. Being *network-centric* means you have the capability to access and employ loosely coupled components that can communicate adequately to coordinate and synchronize. The mere concept of network-centrism, however, doesn't

---

[15] *Business Week,* November 24, 2003.

explain how these components configure an intelligent system capable of achieving the superior competitive results. Information-superior organizations, like the distributed intelligent systems we have described, possess the knowledge and means to accomplish such results. A distributed intelligent system naturally exploits network-centric capabilities to access, task, monitor and control whatever components it needs.

Before leaving this discussion of network-centric systems, we should observe how it relates to the fractal architecture. That architecture considers hierarchically composed components as extremely advantageous building blocks. In an extreme form of network-centric architecture, we might have a completely flat architecture, where no component comprises any other and each communicates with any others it wants to. Email among people operates mostly this way, for example. Such "flat" organizations have attractive qualities. All components have autonomy, they communicate directly as required, and no mediators slow down or add costs to services. In theory, at least, some organizations might perform well if unconstrained by reporting and communication hierarchy

On the other hand, we can find no models of such architectures achieving much sophistication and no examples of social organizations that achieve great results when organized this way. Some groups organized this way do achieve outstanding competitive results, especially high-technology start-up companies. While very small, with staffs well under 50, these companies often seem to work best with a nearly flat reporting structure and free-for-all communications. With 10 employees, for example, nearly everyone needs to know what's going on and probably can directly influence the outcome of every undertaking. By the time the company reaches 50 employees, the cost of open, broadcast communication wears on everybody, and employees routinely demand that management impose some structure, specialize the groups' concerns, and channel communications to minimize overhead for those who don't need to read or hear every message. As companies grow in size, the total volume of messages increases dramatically. The number of possible communicating subgroups among N employees is 2^N, so that with even 50 employees, the number becomes astronomically large. The complexity overwhelms everyone. People can achieve high levels of productivity only by concentrating their energies on a manageable volume of tasks to which they apply their specialized knowledge and skills. To seize the advantages of high productivity, each person can work directly with only a small number of others.

Even within a single living creature, such as any mammal, natural evolution has exploited principles of hierarchy, components, and specialization like those we have postulated for distributed intelligent systems. Cells are a low form of component, comprising other components such as membranes, mitochondria and nuclei. The cells specialize so they can participate in particular types of fluid, tissue or bone, and these in turn combine to form organs, blood, vessels, and bones. These in turn combine to form systems, macro-components that address major functions such as respiration, digestion, and nervous control. Each component participates in one or more higher level component, usually just one at a time, and these components interact with others through interfaces that receive or produce signals or materials. Many scientists have argued that all naturally selected creatures must comprise hierarchical assemblies, because this most efficiently enables natural selection to insure predominance of successful characteristics. [38] [39] Non-hierarchical architectures, on the other hand, don't accumulate and reuse assemblies that partially succeed at satisfying the requirements of life. Efforts to evolve highly competitive creatures with flat architectures can't experiment with even a tiny fraction of the vast number of possible arrangements of parts. Flat-architected creatures are destined to remain small, simple, blind, deaf, and dumb.

So, while network-centric systems allow us to break the constraints that previously made unavoidable rigid, bureaucratic organizations with mostly fixed processes, they shouldn't lead us to think we can compete in complex environments without sophisticated information processing, specialized functions, and components composed of other components. We will employ hierarchical and specialized components, but increasingly we will dynamically configure and assemble them. Improved communications expand the range of organizations we can design and deploy. The organizations that best exploit these opportunities to think efficiently and act agilely will prevail.

Adaptive and Evolutionary Processes

We are all familiar with the ideas of natural selection, attributed mostly to Charles Darwin and the many scientists who have fleshed out the theory. This theory explains how organisms and the species they belong to participate in a competition for survival. The victors in this competition are the species. Individuals come and go, but the species live on as a result of shared genetic material passed from each individual to its offspring. The necessary and sufficient elements for natural selection to work include:

> ➢ Individuals are manifestations of their genetic constituents.

> ➢ When individuals reproduce, they create new individuals with highly similar genetic constitution.

> ➢ Individuals who have advantageous characteristics that enable them to prosper in the environment reproduce more than those without such advantages.

> ➢ Individuals in the same species exchange genetic constituents, usually through sexual reproduction.

> ➢ Some genetic variation occurs in reproduction.

So natural selection works at the level of species, collections of individuals that interact to reproduce and exchange genetic material. As a result, the species builds up a collection of genetic material often called the "gene pool." The gene pool provides the components that generate the components of the individual being. Both the genes themselves and the structures built per their instructions incorporate preferentially selected, hierarchical, component assemblies.

Because natural selection operates on individuals created by reproduction, it doesn't directly operate on long-lived entities such as human organizations or distributed intelligent systems. These systems must incorporate artificial means to evolve so they can prosper in environments continually open to new competitive entrants. That challenge applies in many arenas, including business and war. While no single regimen can assure that every organization evolves effectively and rapidly, the best organizations apply a variety of methods and techniques.

The best known and most comprehensive approach to this challenge in the business and government arena goes by the name *continuous improvement* (CI). Companies try to implement CI through a process usually called a *continuous improvement program* (CIP). CI adapts an organization and its processes in a manner analogous to the way the adaptive-feedback loop changes parameters in a control system. Where the adaptive-feedback loop needs to adjust simple controllable variables such as whether a heater is turned on or off, a CIP can change anything about the organization, its processes, systems or people. This is practically as much power as natural selection applies to members of the species and their genes. Where natural selection can modify genes, scramble them, proliferate well adapted individuals and kill off others, a CIP can make similarly sweeping changes to the organization that employs it.

How do excellent CIPs work? They mimic natural selection. Every part of a business or government system is viewed as a component, assembled from constituents, that provides a function or service to the overall organization. To achieve the best level of competitive fitness, a CIP shapes the organization's performance in the environment by penalizing failure and rewarding success. Failures need to diminish going forward, and successes need to proliferate. Variations of successful components need empirical testing so that even greater successes might result. CIPs must stimulate all of these adaptive responses.

Because CIPs operate on artificial creatures, they can cause adaptations consciously and directly. Successful organizations do that. In addition, intelligent organizations base much of their behavior on explicit world models, so they can use science, knowledge, and reasoning to conjecture ways to reduce failures and improve successes. For example, as we've previously discussed, we can prevent failures by anticipating Murphy, and we can prevent reoccurrences of problems by conjecturing fixes that avoid repeating behaviors that led to previous failures. In addition, we can use our models to conjecture hypotheses about why things work well when success occurs or why some outstanding result pleasantly surprises us. To validate these conjectures, we must conduct experiments, trying various hypotheses to determine how to improve outcomes reliably. Thus, the best organizations consciously view their operations as *living experiments*, looking to predict and explain outcomes, and to allocate most resources to individuals with the greatest expected positive results. A superb organization, such as Procter & Gamble, views its basic evolutionary imperative as a combination of surviving while adapting. It aims to improve its current "breadwinner" products as a way of sustaining returns from previous innovations. Meanwhile, it allocates the maximum possible fraction of its resources to the research and development required to identify its next "breakthrough" product. Such products are found about once a decade. Once a decade is often enough, as it turns out. Almost all cumulative earnings result from the great profits that breakthrough products yield over just a few years. For more than a century, this basic CIP has been at work keeping P&G at the forefront of the most competitive environment in all of business, consumer products.

To be successful in competitive environments, long-lived persistent organizations and systems must employ a CIP to force them to adapt continually. CIPs substitute for the natural selection that enables species to evolve by repeatedly scrambling the genes of individuals and testing out their performance in the environment. Intelligent organizations achieve CI by using knowledge to generate plans, predict outcomes, analyze results, infer causes, improve world models, conjecture and experimentally undertake new approaches, and allocate resources both to exploit successful approaches and to evaluate potential innovations. Efficient thought includes adapting one's knowledge, components, and systems. In this way, intelligent systems do for themselves what natural selection does for species.

Conclusion

This chapter has run a long course, through systems, intelligent systems, humans and machine systems, and distributed intelligent systems. The essential point of this chapter is that critters compete in environments, and the smart ones have terrific advantages. Technology supplies an additional source of leverage that intelligent systems can exploit. We now have means to build organizations and systems that can combine the power of computers and people, across vast distances, to achieve unprecedented levels of efficient thought. That means they can better predict and control their outcomes, can apply resources where and when needed, and can minimize costs associated with delivering their intended products and services. Those that can exploit the technology to think more efficiently, to coordinate and control more quickly and precisely, and to adapt their behavior more successfully will surpass their competitors.

We have reached a turning point in history, where our science, technology, and organizational capabilities combine to make supremacy in this competition attainable and sustainable. Organizations that employ the available technology effectively to extend their reach and hone their efficient thinking skills can achieve unprecedented levels of competitive superiority. These superior entities are the hyper-beings, the focus of the next chapter.

6. Hyper-Beings

Hyper-beings are distributed intelligent systems that attain dominance in their competitive arenas through information superiority. They are unnatural. They span vast spaces, their parts coordinate and synchronize, they adapt blazingly fast, and they outsmart and outperform those who stand in their way. These are not like most organizations known throughout history. These are the likely inheritors of the modern world's riches. Because they surpass all other forms of organization, they reap the greatest profits. The world's resources flow into them and make them stronger still. While we may rue their coming, we really only have two rational responses: try to benefit from them and assure they don't trample us.

They're Coming

Hyper-beings are not some figment of my imagination. They are organizations of unprecedented scale, spanning nations and continents, coordinating, working around the clock, honing their ability to think efficiently and act precisely. These organizations collect information on a real-time basis, assess their plans and expectations, and modify their models as required. While no organization yet has come close to perfecting the mechanisms of efficient thought, the best are inching their way forward and already progressing on all fronts.

Which are the best examples of hyper-beings? The multi-national corporations who have management on one continent, research on another, design on another, production on others, sales and service on others. Companies that produce computer products, such as IBM, HP, and Dell are examples. Cisco, which produces Internet switching equipment, is another. Wal-Mart which dominates retailing in North America and is expanding globally is another. These companies have evolved into *extended enterprises,* coalitions of businesses that come together on as-needed bases to create and deliver this season's products. In the technology sector where many of these companies operate, the high rate of component evolution, rapid product life-cycles, and global appeal of products has forced the businesses to distribute geographically, specialize functions, operate around the clock, and seek lowest-cost resources. Those who try to operate with closely co-located functions, on one continent, simply can't keep up with the torrid pace of global competition. Being small, being self-contained, being vertically integrated has proven to be a recipe for failure. In other sectors, technology has also proved to be a driver, since it has enabled the most advanced

131

companies to coordinate effectively with coalition partners, innovate faster, produce better and cheaper products faster, and achieve great advantages through more intelligent use of resources. The advantage of size and scale is apparent: more capabilities, in more places, means more options for getting things done, and this in turn means the hyper-beings can choose options that give them better, faster and cheaper results than their smaller, less intelligent, and less agile competitors.

In earlier times, some industries benefited from "economies of scale" that allowed them to get more efficient as they got larger. Utility companies, such as gas, power, and telephone had this character. Each of these companies needed to build a network to link its production facility to each of the end-users, and the marginal cost of serving each additional end-user decreased as the size of the in-place network grew. Although there might be a race, ultimately the bigger you were, the more pricing power you had. You could undercut any competition. In the end, the winner took all.

Ultimately, the US Congress and state legislatures passed laws to control monopoly power that emerged from this type of scale-driven superiority. Until the federal court found that Microsoft had attained monopoly status with its PC operating system, the only model we had for economies of scale depended on a physical network infrastructure as in utilities and transportation. Microsoft, on the other hand, illustrates how a hyper-being can take control on a global scale through the complicity of its worldwide partners. Though Microsoft only produces the software, by dint of its market power it has entrained the resources of nearly every computer manufacturer to help establish Microsoft's global hegemony. The partners cooperate on every aspect of creating and delivering business and consumer products, employing global resources, sharing information in near-real time, building and sharing world models, and launching coordinated marketing and sales efforts in every corner of the world. No one can compete with this hyper-being in the markets it dominates.

Another example of the emerging hyper-beings are US-led military coalitions involving small numbers of other countries and large numbers of military and support components. These organizations are assembled primarily by the US Department of Defense on an as-needed basis. Over the last few years DoD has assembled such coalitions for operations in Bosnia, Afghanistan, and Iraq, among others. The US military is actively engaged in the process of transforming from an old-style vertically integrated organization to a network-centric, hyper-being. This transformation has been the focus of several administrations and is well described in DoD publications such as that by Alberts, Garstka and Stein, *Network Centric Warfare: Developing and Leveraging Information Superiority.[40]*

About 15 years ago, most US military operations were divvied up so they could be undertaken by individual services such as the Army or Marines, or by multiple services working on mostly separate sub-missions. Then, the transformation began. The first focus of transformation was on "joint war-fighting," where the individual services (as in "blue" for the Air Force and "green" for the Army) were blended together, to support integrated "purple" joint task forces, led by "purple" joint commanders. From there, the next step of the transformation focused on putting together ad hoc coalitions, again under a unifying joint or coalition commander. The last step of the transformation is underway now. The final step will enable all of these employ distributed intelligent systems to accomplish all missions with flexibility and agility. These intelligent systems exploit network-centric principles to minimize commitment to fixed assets, fixed structure, and fixed doctrine. At the same time, they use the resources and communications capabilities of the network to maximize cunning, speed, agility, precision, and control. In short, this transformation aims to produce an information-superior distributed intelligent system that can attain and assure military supremacy.

There are limits today to what organizations can achieve, relative to their visions and aspirations. We are quite limited in how much intelligence our computer systems implement today. While the World Wide Web provides instant access to a huge amount of information, the web doesn't actually contain the world models hyper-beings need to employ. To apply a world model in planning or analysis, machines must *computationally interpret* it. Computers can interpret computer programs and solve problems with formalized knowledge bases. People can similarly interpret mathematical and qualitative models. However, we cannot, in general, interpret most information, expressed in natural language, without a great deal of human effort. Moreover, the volume of available information relevant to most decisions usually vastly exceeds the person hours for processing it. Thus, the limited amount of formalized knowledge usually limits how much efficient thinking organizations can routinely accomplish. Either the organization has formalized world models that allow it to systemize efficient thought, or the organization works more slowly and less effectively than the hyper-being coming to overtake it.

Today's most sophisticated organizations use a wide variety of specialized tools and languages to encode fragments of what they know and believe. Most of these fragmentary models require humans to apply them to decisions and to interpret their results. Fully automated systems exist, however, for some business processes. For example, many advanced manufacturing companies have highly automated systems for fulfilling purchase orders. These systems translate a received purchase order into a specific production order, identifying specific parts from inventory, and assure that parts and products keep flowing on schedule. While automated, these systems don't usually make the enterprise especially agile. These automated systems require considerable time to implement and primarily address fixed or slowly changing product mixes. Further, they don't report to or directly participate in higher levels of planning and competitive decision-making. Thus, even the most automated, integrated, capable systems in use have barely begun to support the kind of closed-loop efficient thought that's possible. In short, today's most advanced organizations haven't yet climbed far up the efficient thought "learning curve." Considerable challenges remain. In the next subsections, we'll consider how these systems work, what's required to build them, and how you can move your organization incrementally up the curve.

Shape a Salutary Environment

Businesses that have extensive and well managed supply chains most closely approximate the hyper-beings we see coming. Wal-Mart in consumer retail and Dell in personal computers best illustrate this category. Normally, as is the case with Wal-Mart and Dell, the brand owner and retailer control the chain. However, powerful suppliers can also get control of one chain or an entire industry. Such has occurred with the supremacy of Microsoft over the entire PC arena. Regardless of where one's own company fits in one of these extended manufacturing enterprises, each participant acts as a holon within the distributed intelligent system architecture we considered in the previous chapter. We will examine this point in more detail shortly.

Before delving into the mechanics of hyper-beings, however, we need to pause to consider several non-technological issues not yet considered. These include economic, social, psychological and cultural factors that influence the behavior of the human participants within hyper-beings. Most organizations attempt to align a person's economic incentives with organizational goals. Ordinarily, they do this by making an employee's personal compensation contingent on actual performance results. The more intelligent the organization, the easier they find it to motivate the right behaviors economically. These organizations know what they're trying to achieve and how to measure success, so they can reward individual performers for relevant contributions. On the other hand, as the scandals of Enron, Global Crossing, Tyco, and others have shown, individual greed and corporate corruption can play a dominant factor in determining what people and organizations actually do. In this book, we're not going to address these pathologies directly, leaving the important requirements of financial transparency, managerial accountability, and public governance mainly for others. This book focuses on how non-corrupt, appropriately regulated, and effectively governed organizations can achieve unprecedented levels of competitive superiority. Technology is making that possible, but it can't prevent misuse and abuse of power. Civilization also requires an enforced ethical and legal framework.

Just as unethical behavior is a risk to organizations controlled by people, human beings bring along other issues that can make it hard for organizations to achieve their potential. For multi-national distributed intelligent organizations, social, psychological and cultural factors also create. Collectively, these factors create friction that impedes the implementation of efficient thinking. Hyper-beings need their human participants to play specialized roles, collaborate well with others as needed, and pull together across great distances. Increasingly, these people have different backgrounds and speak different languages. They have different styles of interaction. Their preferences for when, where and how they work differ.

All of these personal differences limit the organization's ability to orchestrate and coordinate thinking and action. For these reasons, hyper-beings actively strive to produce a unified organizational culture based on the processes and knowledge required to coordinate effectively. Only those organizations that find effective ways to diminish the personal, social and cultural sources of difference will become dominant hyper-beings.

Because hyper-beings have so many competitive advantages, we will see a continuing homogenization of cultures among the participants in the dominant hyper-being organizations. Differences in values will diminish. Spoken language will standardize on English. Measurement and compensation will become more uniform. "If you can't beat 'em, join 'em" will be the dominant logic for those who have any choice.

Speaking personally, I'm not a fan of homogenized culture. I have a preference for diverse experiences and environments. But, frankly, preferences like these have negligible impact on competitively driven evolution. If enough consumers and tourists spend their dollars on heterogeneous foods, products, and locales, then the consumer product and tourism hyper-beings will make sure they're always available. Otherwise, cultural diversity will suffer the same rapid decline as biodiversity has.

The last impediment to hyper-being dominance that we should consider is human opposition, which can be based on any number of grounds. Local retailers oppose "big box" stores such as Wal-Mart, because they destroy their businesses. Local urban planners oppose them too, because the giant stores increase driving to the suburbs, pave over large amounts of green space, and kill off the tax base of the urban centers. Labor groups oppose multi-nationals and their outsourcing, because their actions reduce salaries and benefits and generally weaken environmental and labor standards. Some Muslim fundamentalists oppose all of Western materialism, and the behemoth hyper-beings are the heavyweight champions of our capitalist system. Europeans oppose globalism, because it floods their countries with American consumer brands that grab customer dollars and torque native tastes away from traditional qualities. In short, hyper-beings achieve many of their benefits by leaving high-priced labor behind and subordinating traditional cultural values to new ones, more aligned with their economic interests.

Is all this "progress" really good? Well, it won't be without some counter-balancing actions. For example, the world community might implement programs to mitigate individual and community losses that result when hyper-beings conquer traditional businesses. The Princeton economist Robert Shiller has proposed a number of risk-sharing approaches for big social challenges like these in his book *The New Financial Order.[41]* His basic idea is that we ought to create "insurance" products that allow participants in large economic systems to hedge their bets, thereby providing some cushion for those dumped by "economic progress." It's clear from the increasing concentration of wealth, including the disparity between the world's top 5% and the bottom 50%, that the current vehicle of progress, namely unbridled capitalism, will one day cause an explosive revolt. It seems obvious that the viability of the hyper-beings themselves will ultimately depend on their self-interested recognition of the need to mitigate such disparities. We should expect to see some significant changes in social welfare and business governance on a global basis as the dominant entities perceive growing threats to their own security. Progressive policies will probably seem wiser to them than programs of either "benign neglect" or coercive suppression.

In the end, every organization must motivate its human players to help the organization perform. For this reason, hyper-beings need to impress their own employees with good community relations and social beneficence. This need should drive hyper-beings inexorably to promote progressive policies across the global environment. Once dominant companies understand that they must shape the environment to keep it from becoming lethal, they can act decisively. As an example, consider the recent turnabout of the timber company Boise-Cascade, a longtime target of environmentalists. Virtually overnight it did a 180-degree about-face, "changing its spots." Becoming a vanguard environmentalist made excellent sense once the management perceived that yesterday's self-centered policies would undermine their future viability in a global market with more entwined sensibilities:

> Boise Cascade Corp. agreed to stop buying wood products from the world's endangered forests, bowing to the kind of intense pressure from customers and environmental activists that is increasingly leading forest-products purveyors to adopt greener practices.
>
> ...The Boise, Idaho, timber concern said it will end purchases of wood from endangered forests in places like Chile, Indonesia and Canada as such areas are mapped. Next year, Boise Cascade said, it will stop cutting timber from virgin forests in the U.S.
>
> Meanwhile, the company said it will also start pressuring its suppliers to follow its lead, such as by giving purchasing preference to ones that provide paper and wood products from forests that are independently certified as being under healthy management. To help enforce the new policy, Boise said it will start tracking the origins of paper and wood products it receives.
>
> — *Wall Street Journal*, September 3, 2003

In short, hyper-beings are such dominant players, they must model their own impact on the environment and shape it, rather than passively assume it will remain habitable and desirable. All rational beings must expect to do better in a salutary environment than in a toxic one. The "environment" of the hyper-being comprises practically the entire Earth and all of the communities in which it operates. Policies that offend people turn those people into unsatisfactory customers, suppliers, partners, regulators, and employees. As a result, the hyper-being seeks effective ways to assure that people in all of its constituencies will like it and admire it. Efficient thought and ambitious economic objectives should combine to spur hyper-beings to find ways to "do well by doing good."

Tools and Methods

Hyper-beings need tools and methods to implement distributed intelligent systems that enable them to operate. The heart of these systems is a set of capabilities for efficient thought performed by holonic components distributed over wide spaces, communicating via networks. Supply chain management is an excellent example of the best practices in use by today's hyper-beings. In these chains, each company must tie its own planning and control functions into the network of companies that cooperate in the extended enterprise. They use a variety of tools and products to accomplish this integration. Each business unit provides interfaces to the others it interacts with for procuring and providing desired products and services. An example will help illustrate how they do this.

Table 2. Principal Systems Used in Extended Manufacturing Enterprises.

Software Application Category	Principal Functions
Design (e.g., CAD, eCAD, mCAD)	Develop detailed product designs
Engineering & Process Planning	Develop good production processes
Product Data Management (PDM)	Manage all product data needed for production and maintenance
Planning (MRP, MRP-II)	Develop production plans and determine associated resource requirements
Sourcing & Purchasing	Select suppliers and obtain needed supplies from them
Stock Management	Keep track of stock and inventory and assure

	replenishment as needed
Retailing	Make goods available for purchase by end-customers and capture all relevant data about purchase transactions
e-Commerce	Enable purchase transactions to be conducted entirely via Internet
Order Entry	Log and validate purchase orders to initiate fulfillment activities
Manufacturing	Make products per design and process specifications
Logistics	Provide resources and finished goods where needed
Shipping & Tracking	Move resources and keep account of their location
Budgeting	Determine resources required to achieve plans and allocate them
Accounting	Track financial transactions and determine results by categories of interest

A company such as Dell Computer sells computers usually in small quantities to individuals who place orders through the Dell website. Dell offers specialized websites to its most important customers, such as the US Government. A variety of system components participate in supporting the initial interaction with the prospective customer. Such components perform the following services: display and promote available models; price the computers, options, shipping and tax; determine availability in inventory or time to assemble; determine shipping times and delivery dates; accept and book the order. With the advent of distributed computing and web services, each of these functions can be done by specialized software, operating on one of many alternative servers, each linked opportunistically to complete the needed transaction.

By the time a specific computer is offered for sale, Dell has already established linkages with a range of companies to perform the actions it doesn't do itself. Every step in the production process is contracted out to a supplier, and these suppliers in turn contract out the tasks of inventory management for subassemblies and components. Excellent systems provide "visibility" of the supply chain to each organization that has a "need to know." This enables Dell to commit to delivery dates and prices, because the visibility enables it to see current schedules and predict future results. Specialized models translate ordered products into assemblies and components, production and shipping steps, charges and payments. Table 2 above identifies a set of software application categories commonly used by extended manufacturing enterprises. Hyper-beings certainly use these, and others as well, to automate much of the efficient thought that enables them to bring their products from concepts to the customer. Recently, for example, Dell has taken the final step of automation, eliminating most humans from the final production processes, as this recent news article explains[16]:

> Somebody tell Dell to slow down. Just as the rest of the computer industry is finally catching on to Dell's vaunted e-commerce techniques, the Round Rock (Tex.) company is pioneering the next level of Web- based automation.
>
> At Dell's plant in Nashville, online orders go directly to assembly- line robots, which fetch all the parts to create a custom-built PC. The company's one-year-old system automatically loads software onto the hard drives and tests the machines before an army of robots boxes them up for shipping.
>
> Dell's new setup requires half as many workers as before, and it runs at three times the speed. It churns out one computer every four seconds. Dell is hurrying to automate its eight other plants. Just what the panting competition feared.
>
> The Payoff: The automated assembly line pumps out 900 computers an hour, vs. 300 before. Output is up 40%.

Because most of the electronics companies participate in various industry-oriented standard-setting groups such as the Rosetta Net Consortium and OASIS, they have developed standard models of products, purchasing, production, and electronic commerce. These standards usually use XML to represent community-specific descriptions of important semantic objects in the electronics domain. At present, proposed standards exist for many e-business processes and for the description of electronic components. These modern standards build on earlier more limited success around electronic data

---

[16] *Business Week,* November 24, 2003.

interchange (EDI) standards that supported more limited classes of business-to-business transactions. The new standards attempt to reflect more understanding of business transactions, so they can exchange more information and establish more agile relationships.

These XML-encoded standards define the language different partners in a supply chain use to exchange information. Establishing a new language takes time and effort. These modern standards take time initially to specify how to express things and what they mean. Then the standards efforts require additional time to win acceptance in principle from a critical mass of community participants. Finally, still more time passes before the new standard become the dominant means of communicating in practice. The latency incurred in implementing standardized communication reflects both technological immaturity and business friction. The immaturity results from the general lack of community experience in formulating shareable models of business processes and products. When companies were less distributed and more vertically integrated, each company could determine for itself and by itself how best to describe things. As companies virtually dissolved into collections of components participating in various extended enterprises, the need to communicate increased but the relative power of each participant to shape affairs decreased. For this reason, each company participates in industry-wide efforts somewhat reluctantly, figuring that a slow pace of standardization won't really hurt it. They reason that everyone can get more efficient together, albeit at a leisurely pace.

This technological immaturity allows most companies to participate patiently in the decade-long efforts to standardize inter-company communications and coordination. Against this complacent friction, dominant businesses push aggressively. The more dominant the company, the more opportunity it sees in increasing efficiency across the entire supply chain. Thus, very dominant players, such as Wal-Mart, Cisco, and Intel, push their suppliers to accept and implement proposed standards much faster. Once one dominant hyper-being, such as Wal-Mart or Dell, successfully implements standardized communication to support a significant fraction of its overall activities, it increases its advantages over its competitors. A recent brief news report in *Business Week* (Nov. 24, 2003) illustrates the power of the giants to make their components hew the line they specify:

Wal-Mart

The Project: Push its 100 top suppliers to use "smart tags" embedded in product cases to track much of what the discounter sells.

The Payoff: Knowing where every item is, and keeping shelves stocked. Analysts expect Wal-Mart to reap pretax savings of as much as $8 billion by 2007.

Leading the way in the so-called smart-tags revolution, Wal-Mart Stores (WMT) Inc. has asked its biggest suppliers to start using the radio-controlled inventory tags on everything from cases of Coke to pallets of Dove soap. Wal-Mart hopes to track inventory better, reduce the number of out-of-stock products, and most important, boost sales, because the right product will be in the right place at the right time. Now other retailers will have to follow Wal-Mart's lead.

Small companies desperately want to be chosen as a key supplier to several dominant customers, but they find this extremely challenging. The dominant hyper-beings generally don't wait for industry-wide standards to implement their systems. Each one requires that all of their suppliers must bear the cost of adapting their systems to accord with the interfaces defined by that dominant. Before industry standards settle, these interfaces reflect idiosyncratic aspects of the hyper-being's own processes. So while each small company realizes that its own health depends on having multiple customers, they often find it too expensive to adapt their systems and support more than one demanding task master. Thus, the small company most needs the industry standard solutions and can least afford to contribute to their establishment. This further enhances the dominant player's purchasing power.

A hyper-being such as Wal-Mart implements IT systems today for most of its activities. It models its customers and their preferences. It conducts research to develop new products that it expects should appeal to them. It tests these experimental products in its stores. It assesses results against expectations and feeds back information and resources accordingly. It integrates suppliers globally. It manufactures nothing itself. It achieves greater efficiency in thinking and execution than any of its competitors. It's already the largest retailer in the world and is growing faster than the competition.

In short, companies have morphed into components of extended enterprises. These extended enterprises aspire to be distributed intelligent systems. The best of these have already become hyper-beings. They have attained such dominant positions of superiority that they will continue to grow and succeed, beyond any enterprise in history.

Competitive Advantages

Size has not always been an advantage, and although hyper-beings are vast in scale, size *per se* is not what makes them successful. The competitive advantages of hyper-beings are mainly these:

1. They earn better results, because they advantageously and effectively exploit more specialized components.

2. They produce goods at services at lower cost, because they employ efficient thought and integrate more low-cost components.

3. They can deliver results faster, because they are agile in configuring and employing components and can coordinate them effectively over large distances.

4. They use their dominant positions to coerce components to adhere to mandated standards, thereby reducing friction and improving integration.

5. They use their dominant positions to extract the best possible economic terms from components and customers.

These five advantages are huge. They assure "the rich get richer," as applied to market dominant hyper-beings. In sum, these advantages mean the superior hyper-being can offer better products and services at prices below what its competitors can offer. From the point of view of the hyper-being, getter better is part of a virtuous cycle: the better you get, the more dominant you are, which enables you to do better still.

Disadvantages and Vulnerabilities

Just as size is not always an advantage, it can frequently be a disadvantage. But as we've said before, large size results from the hyper-being's success, rather than causing it. So once the organization grows very large, its very size can pose a threat. When we contemplate how hyper-beings might fail, we see the following principal weaknesses:

1. Power corrupts, and really powerful organizations breed corrupt leaders.

2. Success and dominance breed smugness and laziness.

3. Hyper-beings depend on advanced technology and infrastructure, and these are vulnerable to attack and disruption.

4. Continued dominance depends on continuing innovation, but big enterprises often fail miserably at this.

5. Efficient thought requires open minds, honest analysis, transparency and creativity, but people in power often prefer to impose tight control and avoid challenging questions.

Thus, the greatest risk hyper-beings face is that they will become bureaucratic, arrogant, corrupt, spoiled, pig-headed and stuck in the past. These concerns are not idle. Every large organization is full of people more concerned with protecting their own "rice bowl" than improving the organization's performance. This self-centeredness arises naturally, because individual humans make most decisions and personal concerns often dominate our considerations. To limit the influence of such personal factors, traditional organizations imposed rigid structures and decision processes. Large businesses found that such rigid business approaches worked satisfactorily when little innovation occurred, political deals protected domestic markets, and opponents lacked adequate resources to muster serious challenges.

In looking forward, we can safely predict that a number of dominant hyper-beings will succumb to the sclerotic effects of bureaucracy, politics, corruption, smugness, arrogance and laziness. Once big growth companies devolve first into former growth companies, then into commodity companies, and then they literally disappear. Think of Digital, Data General, and Compaq as familiar examples in the computing industry. Even companies in old established markets, such as P&G in consumer products, have to run for their lives every day. If they don't hustle, those big innovations needed every decade to rejuvenate profits and enhance leadership don't show up in time.

Hyper-beings have one intrinsic reason that they might successfully evade these lethal threats: efficient thinking is an anti-sclerotic remedy. Efficient thought requires a persistent, open, critical review of one's own world model. It demands that you compare actual results to plans' expected results and assign credit and blame where appropriate. Further, it demands that you innovate, conjecturing and experimentally evaluating plausible ways to solve problems, thwart Murphy, and seize new opportunities. Any organization that systematizes these activities will achieve greater objectivity than has been true of earlier organizations, and that objectivity can prove a potent antidote to the greatest dangers a hyper-being faces. Efficient thought has its own logic, and it objectively reinforces positive contributions.

Follow the Leaders

Many outstanding companies and organizations are actively trying to transform their enterprises into hyper-beings. The network-centric warfare concept of the US Department of Defense, for example, provides a high-level vision and rough blueprint for turning the US military into a hyper-being shell, one that can be fully populated by diverse components from allies and coalition partners as needed to accomplish ad hoc missions[40]. The DoD understands that it wants information superiority and an ability to use that to create better plans, execute them more precisely, and do all of that faster and cheaper than ever before. The DoD envisions developing new high-level directives, plus doctrine, tactics, systems and processes that all support this vision. They expect this transformation to take time, experimentation, and evolution. Yet, even with only the rudimentary abilities to share models, communicate, and coordinate now in hand, the US already has achieved dominance in this competitive arena. By focusing on efficient thought and agility, the US will further enhance its supremacy.

Dominant businesses with modern IT capabilities, such as Wal-Mart, FedEx and Dell, continue to extend their systems to support improvements in efficient thought and agile execution. They extensively model their business, addressing issues ranging from suppliers through customers. They adopt and exploit new technologies and methods sooner and more effectively than competitors. They strive continually to enrich their world models, share and reuse knowledge more frequently, and improve collaboration and coordination. They systematize situation assessment and planning functions, test and validate the knowledge used in these functions, and conduct research to improve their ability to predict and explain events accurately. They allocate extensive resources and management attention to the development and experimental evaluation of new products, processes and services. They seek continually higher levels of product and process quality, and they practice continuous improvement diligently.

Lagging companies appear hamstrung by the difficulty of justifying potential IT projects, finding it difficult to quantify the hoped-for benefits. Meanwhile, the dominant hyper-beings move aggressively. These advanced organizations have an excellent understanding of where gaps in their knowledge and errors in their processes hurt them. They know that knowledge fuels their processes and makes them predictable. They can quickly estimate and qualitatively appreciate how proposed systems would increase model accuracy, reduce process errors, and reduce resource wastage. They continually seek ways to move their organizations further up the scale of distributed intelligence. For the would-be hyper-being, the strategic direction seems very clear, and they value all significant steps in that direction.

Many smaller, less-dominant companies these days see their best strategic options as participating in *collaborative commerce*, business accomplished by *ad hoc* "extended enterprises." One company may win a major supply contract from Ford for its new pick-up truck one day, and the next season it might become a key component of a GM project. Ford and GM use different tools and methods, so the supplier needs to support different interfaces, share different data models, and support different visibility requirements. Any company that can provide specialized component functions to different hyper-beings at low cost should earn great profits. But any company will most likely incur significant costs in their efforts to integrate with the proprietary systems employed by each hyper-being. This is a kind of "technical" friction that slows down collaboration and drives up cost.

In the minds of all companies thinking about collaborative commerce, standards seem desirable, since they can reduce the friction that impedes participation. From the viewpoint of the dominant players, this means more components can compete to supply needed services, giving the dominant player pricing power. From the viewpoint of the smaller players, this means they can join ad hoc coalitions at lower cost, potentially allowing them to participate in multiple successful business ventures. For these reasons, each industry area is working on standards that can simplify e-business and collaborative commerce. Many collaborative ventures will be undertaken. A few will succeed. A very small number of hyper-beings will hit the jackpot, attaining clear supremacy in their arenas.

Implementing and Evolving Information-Superior Systems

Let's assume you're in an organization that aspires to move up the evolutionary ladder, improving its thinking efficiency, and evolving toward hyper-being status. Depending on how far your organization has already progressed, different next steps will be appropriate. All organizations need to evolve through a "spiral process," making some changes, trying them out, evaluating them, and then starting the cycle again. As the organization evolves towards information superiority, it will need to progress across each of the following dimensions:

1. Products and skills of efficient thought.

2. Componentization of specialized services.

3. Distributed communication and collaboration.

4. Agile configuration and use of resources.

The tables below illustrate how organizations can progress through increasing levels of capability on each dimension. Each table considers just one dimension at a time. It considers various aspects of the corresponding dimension, how to characterize the current level of capability and, for each level, suggests specific actions the organization can take to move towards a higher level.

The first table below, Table 3, aggregates the key capabilities of efficient thought into just four principal categories: world model, situation assessment, planning, and continuous improvement. This aggregation simplifies the presentation and should make it easier to grasp what types of steps produce what kinds of improvement.

Table 3. Incremental Steps to Improve Efficient Thought.

Capability Assessed	Current Capability Level	Improvement Objective	Action to Achieve Improvement
World Model	Unwritten	Initiate world model-based processes	Choose an initial high-value area, capture and share the knowledge, and use it in at least one process
	Informal	Formalize using a computer-interpretable language	Adopt a modeling language appropriate to the area and automate the application of knowledge to at least one process
	Significantly incomplete	Increase coverage	Choose the next highest-value area, formalize the knowledge, and use it

		Not validated	Validate the knowledge	Experimentally test beliefs
Situation Assessment		Ad hoc or unsystematic	Initiate systematic process	Identify an observable area that impacts the organization's results significantly, monitor it, and learn to predict and explain events
		Significantly incomplete	Increase coverage	Choose the next highest-value area, and extend the situation assessment process to cover this area
		Significantly inaccurate	Increase validity	Scientifically investigate alternative models to find ones that predict and explain events more accurately
Planning		Ad hoc or unsystematic	Initiate systematic process	Identify a behavioral result that impacts the organization's objectives significantly, generate and evaluate alternative plans for producing it, forecast likely outcomes, and choose the best
		Significantly incomplete	Increase coverage	Choose the next highest-value behavioral result and extend the process to cover this aspect
		Significantly suboptimal results attained	Increase effectiveness	Conjecture new or modified beliefs that enable plans to generate better options, and empirically evaluate those conjectures in future trials

	Actual results vary significantly from planned results	Increase accuracy and validity	Determine where the forecast of expected outcomes deviated from actual, diagnose, conjecture fixes, and empirically validate these in future trials
Continuous Improvement Process	Ad hoc or unsystematic	Initiate systematic process	Determine a required performance level resulting from some process, measure attained level, and alter the process as required to assure consistent satisfactory results
	Informal	Formalize	Adopt a process specification language appropriate to the area and automate at least steps for data collection, analysis and reporting
	Stagnant results	Raise the bar	Set higher quality goals, such as 5-sigma or 6-sigma, to challenge the organization to learn to excel
	Disappointing financial results	Benchmark, compare, reallocate & innovate	Measure company activities and results in comparison to industry norms and leaders, conjecture innovative ways to improve, and empirically test those that equal or exceed best performers

As Table 3 indicates, organizations can improve their capabilities along several dimensions, and progress incrementally moves the organization from informal, unwritten, and ad hoc practices toward formalized, model-based, automated, systematic, performance-oriented, and empirically validated ones. These practices and the need for continuously improvement them occur in most areas of traditional management and engineering and in all industries.

For example, leading businesses in the commodities of energy, chemicals, and paper operate at high levels of process maturity. Their processes change relatively slowly, because their environments are relatively stable.

Many companies, especially young ones, compete in younger industries, operating in more dynamic environments, and continually absorbing rapidly evolving technology. These businesses generally don't employ mature processes. They find it difficult to take time and transfer resources from front-line business tasks of product development, manufacturing, sales and marketing. As these companies grow and prosper, they begin to take incremental steps to improve elements of efficient thought. Often, the first steps are driven by problems in product quality, causing high warranty costs or poor reviews that threaten future sales. As they work their way from the symptoms of poor processes, they learn that decisions early in the product life-cycle have the most impact and afford the greatest leverage for improvement. They realize they have unsystematic processes, relying on informal or non-validated knowledge. In short, they learn the need for efficient thought the hard way. Meantime, the competitors with more mature processes often overtake them, as they find it somewhat easy to copy a competitive offering, reverse engineer it, and beat the originator on quality and cost.

Many organizations over the last decade have participated actively in initiatives that aim squarely at improving efficient thought. Knowledge management efforts aim to capture world model knowledge from enterprise constituents, formalize and index it to some extent, and make it easy for others to access and employ it. Five-sigma and six-sigma programs have focused companies on trying to reduce process errors or faults in results to 1 in 100,000 or 1 in a million. Making processes so precise, eliminating their variability, has many positive effects on quality, cost, and profits. Other approaches that have focused on related quality issues as drivers of overall results have included Total Quality Management (TQM)[42] and Quality Function Deployment (QFD)[43]. Each of these encourages organizations to identify key qualities they should address. The methods suggest ways to design products that will achieve these qualities. They also define continuous improvement processes that can move results incrementally closer to goals [44].

Hyper-beings understand the importance of these capabilities, use the best available tools and methods to formalize their knowledge and processes, and use extensive amounts of computing to automate much of the work of efficient thought. They don't consider such use of IT a luxury, because it gives them superiority in the meta-processes that continually upgrade and improve the efficiency of their thought. Those improvements, in turn, propel them to superiority in daily competition.

Table 4, below, describes how components become increasingly specialized and easily employed by multiple processes and organizations. Increased specialization feeds competitive advantage. In addition to specializing, components need to integrate into higher-level components. To integrate easily and smoothly, they must fit into various frameworks that provide the scaffolding for multi-component integration. Components vary in the quality of their services and products, and so do overall systems. The best components have proven qualities and work well as part of overall systems that assure global properties, such as responsiveness, availability, and security. The table suggests specific actions organizations can take to make themselves or their components more attractive to hyper-beings.

Table 4. Incremental Steps to Improve Componentry.

Capability Assessed	Current Capability Level	Improvement Objective	Action to Achieve Improvement
Modularity	Little or none	Initiate modularization	Choose an initial high-value capability, separate it, and give users access to it in your environment
	Rudimentary and proprietary	Standardize components and reuse them	Focus efforts on providing and using components that have broad appeal in the market
	Mature and standardized	Standardize services and reuse them	Adopt a service-based standard and make the capabilities available to remote service users

	Adequate for remote service	Attain best-of-breed status	Offer services as widely as possible, challenge competitors, and become widely known as best
Openness of Interfaces	Little or none	Offer easy-to-use components	Adopt an interface style that's easy for others to implement, such as *wrapping*, and help others employ it
	Proprietary	Adopt and employ open standards	Choose an open standard for component interfaces and adapt components to comply
	Open and standardized	Increase adoption	Hone components to excel in biggest open markets with widest population of users
Agility of Framework	Little or none	Provide initial capability for flexible use of components	Identify an aspect of variety that affords high-value flexibility and design a framework that parameterizes choices or accepts plug-ins to implement variants
	Accepts parameters or plug-ins in pre-defined roles	Increase dimensions of flexibility	Factor additional services out of the framework, either into complementary frameworks, or into partitioned service layers
	Easily incorporates new services or capabilities	Modularize responsibilities for assuring key qualities	Create complementary frameworks to support quality attributes and make it easy to combine them with other frameworks

	Assures total system quality attributes	Validate frameworks and increase adoption	Test and validate frameworks over diverse environments to demonstrate performance and robustness
Quality of Components	Undetermined	Initiate quality assurance	Develop test suites and automate testing processes to measure as-built quality
	Tested	Gain acceptance	Formalize use scenarios and develop objective metrics
	Empirically benchmarked	Establish superiority	Experiment and publish analyses
	Scientifically validated and assured	Maintain superiority while improving	Constrain new component releases by very high quality improvement hurdles

As Table 4 indicates, many challenges stand in the way of creating, improving, and employing excellent components within agile organizations. The best components can act independently, deploy wherever and whenever needed, work effectively with other components, self-synchronize, and contribute to overall concerns such as security. To evolve components we must identify valued capabilities, package them in ways that others find easy to use, and demonstrate their advantages both through widespread adoption and empirical methods. These are daunting requirements for several reasons. First, we can compose systems in many different ways, so we may not know the best way to modularize components. Second, different suppliers offer similar capabilities, so characterizing and comparing the various offerings can require considerable effort. Third, integrated systems manifest many overall quality attributes, and we may not know how to value these or the best way to trade-off one against another.

Occasionally a component supplier can effectively achieve superiority in all of these dimensions. Intel has done that in the microprocessor arena, for example. As another example of recent progress, consider the flash-RAM memory card. Manufacturers are turning these cards into successful, standardized components in a wide variety of consumer products. Companies such as FedEx and UPS have made their delivery services standardized outsourced components of many enterprises. As a recent illustration, consider this recent news item about UPS[17]:

> Package going out? Talk to the receptionist. That's a tired refrain United Parcel Service (UPS) Inc. is eager to end with its new CampusShip service, workers can now operate virtual post offices on their desktops. Whether in the office or on the road, an employee can track a package, print labels, build an online address list, and e-mail shipping notifications. So workers don't send Grandma in Alaska a box of chocolates on the company's dime, CampusShip lets managers set rules on who can ship what. Use of the free service, which is bundled in with other UPS services customers buy, has grown 20% in the past three months alone, for a total of 300,000 users at 6,000 companies. If this goes on much longer, mailroom employees may soon go the way of elevator operators.

Hyper-beings are most concerned with employing superb components, with as much agility as possible. Therefore, they encourage their suppliers, partners and business units to make steady progress on all paths described in Table 4. They create incentives for the best component providers, and they abandon the laggards.

Because hyper-beings operate as distributed collaborative holarchic organizations, they need to employ best possible techniques for collaborating and communicating. While most technical people think of "communications" as primarily concerning the quality and bandwidth of connections, that narrow perspective overlooks higher-level and important facets. *Communication*, in its everyday sense, means *transmitting and sharing ideas*. A "pipe" that moves bits is a prerequisite, but little more. Collaborating effectively means combining multiple viewpoints and problem-solving capabilities to arrive at better solutions than the individuals could achieve alone. Most organizations don't really do well at collaboration. Traditional hierarchical organizations, operating in relatively static environments, didn't feel the pressure to solve problems across organizational boundaries frequently. That era has ended, however. These days, hyper-beings realize that they must routinely collaborate across historical boundaries to make their *ad hoc* coalitions, virtual organizations, and extended enterprises work efficiently.

---

[17] *Business Week,* November 24, 2003.

Table 5, below, looks at four aspects of distributed collaboration to prescribe how organizations can climb the ladder of improvement. These capability aspects include: bandwidth and connection; language and protocol; alignment of perceptions; and synchronicity of actions. Bandwidth and connectivity define the capability to exchange bits, and such a capability can improve in many ways. Language and protocol combine to determine how well collaborators can express what they mean and successfully convey their intent. These elements become more specialized and effective as they mature. All collaborators hope to align perceptions. People may hold idiosyncratic points of view and interpretations of events that determine their individual perceptions. Until collaborators understand one another's perceptions, they have difficulty understanding what the others already believe and what they intend to convey when they say something related to those beliefs. Once mutually understood, collaborators try to maintain this alignment of perceptions. Often, collaborative decision-making results in coordinated action, and this often requires them to synchronize their behaviors. They may predetermine the planned timing of actions, but execution often requires adaptive control to deal with delays and other deviations from the plan's expectations.

The elements in Table 5 illustrate how to assess an organization's current level of capability and how to undertake programs that incrementally improve them. Ultimately, hyper-beings will achieve excellence across all four aspects.

Table 5. Incremental Steps to Improve Distributed Collaboration.

Capability Assessed	Current Capability Level	Improvement Objective	Action to Achieve Improvement
Bandwidth and Connectivity	Inadequate bandwidth	Greatly reduce constraint and latency	Purchase more private bandwidth, use more public bandwidth, or reduce low priority uses
	Limited mobility	Provide access almost everywhere	Exploit Internet access points with dynamic configuration, including wireless hotspots

	Intermittent connectivity	Assure almost continuous connectivity	Increase availability and access, utilize reliable and robust technologies; cache needed data for disconnected operation
	Low security	Increase communication security	Use private networks including virtual private networks (VPNs) to restrict access; encrypt traffic
Language and Protocol	Informal language	Standardize vocabulary and message types	Identify what's important to know and communicate; adopt an explicit catalog of terms, parameters, assertions and other messages to communicate with
	Informal protocol	Standardize interactions	Identify the important types of multi-step interactions, and adopt a formalized process for each type
	Inefficient communication procedures	Communicate efficiently	Identify redundant and low-value communications and eliminate or reduce these; conversely, identify high-value communication opportunities and increase these

	Informal and *ad hoc*	Adopt systematic processes	Implement standardized processes for creating, representing, and sharing assessments of important facts, hypotheses and intentions
Alignment of Perceptions	Infrequent	Achieve near continuous alignment	Adopt processes to recompute assessments periodically or to update them as events arise
	Incomplete	Align nearly completely	Identify differences in beliefs that lead to divergent judgments or account for execution errors; resolve these and include revised concepts in on-going alignments
	Inefficient	Increase communication productivity	Measure the value-added of each message and associated process, giving priority to highest valued ones and eliminating lowest valued ones

Synchronicity of Actions	*Ad hoc* or unsystematic	Adopt systematic processes	Associate standard time properties with key planned actions, such as earliest and latest start times, earliest and latest finish times, and comparative timing relations with prerequisite and contemporaneous actions; use these to determine acceptable execution times
	Highly limited range of synchronizable behaviors	Make the times of nearly all planned actions controllable	Select plan times that satisfy all constraints, including some schedule slack; monitor progress reports to assure continued acceptability; adjust planned times for remaining actions as needed
	Imprecise and errorful	Set high process quality goals and meet them	Set higher quality goals, such as 5-sigma or 6-sigma, to challenge the organization to learn to excel; analyze and reduce variability in the time each process step uses
	Difficult and expensive	Simplify and automate	Implement a framework that supports planning and control of time requirements

Table 6 makes one major point: high-productivity communication exploits available bandwidth to make significant changes in situation assessments and planned actions. To achieve this kind of productivity we have to prioritize resources and activities to convey important information and think through its consequences. In most organizations today, this is almost the opposite of actual practice. Because humans find almost any repetitive task reinforcing[45], they communicate excessively, especially about insignificant things. As an example, it's easy to compose and to read email messages, so many low value messages circulate. On the other hand, it's difficult to identify new information and to develop important new information, so people often spend inadequate time and effort on producing high-value communications. In addition, many organizations have poor methods of uniting related bits of information into a single shared and comprehensive model, so too many related and overlapping messages circulate. On top of these problems, people don't naturally or easily appreciate the intricacies of sequence, concurrency, and dependency among activities every time they formulate or adjust a plan. The result of this is that most organizations achieve a mediocre level of collaborative productivity.

In fact, human groups frequently exhibit two alternate pathologies. In the first case, they doggedly hold onto the first plan they formulate, even when new information should make them reject it. In the second case, they think and act shallowly. In this case, they repeatedly latch onto new half-baked plans when salient new information makes them doubt their previous conclusion. Against such mediocre planners, the hyper-beings will easily prevail. Hyper-beings understand that time spent on low-value work is truly wasted, while effort spent achieving superior results directly advances their supremacy. As Table 6 shows, there are many concrete actions organizations can implement to achieve the disciplined level of coordination possible. In coordinating distributed operations, the disciplined soundly trounce the complacent.

The final dimension we want to consider during this discussion of how organizations can move incrementally up the ladder of competency concerns agile configuration and resource utilization. In this area, organizations strive to assemble rapidly whatever they need to do the current job from the best resources available. When we visualize organizations as they developed in the 20th century, to standardize processes so they could efficiently mass produce standardized products, we can see that the dynamic hyper-being differs dramatically. We want to have our cake and eat it too: we want an ability to configure flexibly to accomplish nearly any mission and, at the same time, we want to achieve extraordinary levels of efficiency that usually require large-scale standardization. Hyper-beings learn this magic, by improving their ability to rapidly access, configure, employ and control resources assembled on an *ad hoc* basis.

The table below breaks out four aspects of this talent and shows how you can incrementally move your organization to higher levels on each. These four aspects include: resource and capability modeling, resource fungibility, logistical agility, and control of actions. Modeling resources means describing the various replaceable units, the utility they provide and prerequisites for employing them. This may be simple, as in the case of various hardware "widgets," or very difficult, as in the case of complex resources such as military units or suppliers. Modeling capabilities means understanding what process steps are required to produce desired results and, in turn, understanding what capabilities resources provide that can accomplish these steps. Modeling resources and capabilities enables us to consider different configurations for performing each job.

Fungible resources can substitute for one another, either because they satisfy similar input requirements or possess alternative capabilities for playing a needed role. Making resources fungible and available takes work. First, we must assure that they really do satisfy common requirements. Second, we must arrange matters to assure that we can procure these resources quickly when needed.

Logistical agility means that we can get resources where needed quickly and efficiently, without enormous amounts of inventory. Traditional logistical systems usually tie up huge amounts of money in inventory, involve long supply chains, and adapt slowly to meet changing requirements.

Control of actions assures that actions happen correctly: where they should, when they should, and how they should. Precise control prevents errors, waste, and even many mission failures.

Organizations must work on all of these aspects to improve their organizational agility and competitiveness. Table 6 describes specific programs that can produce incremental improvement in each of these areas.

Table 6. Incremental Steps to Improve Agile Configuration and Resource Use.

Capability Assessed	Current Capability Level	Improvement Objective	Action to Achieve Improvement
Resource and Capability Modeling	Informal	Formalize using a computer-interpretable language	Focus on resource categories offering the greatest potential advantages for increased agility; adopt and employ standard resource and capability models and modeling languages if available
	Significantly incomplete	Increase coverage	Choose the next highest-value categories, formalize the models, and employ them
	Too coarse-grained	Unbundle resources, and refine models	Identify resources or capabilities where finer-grained modularity would afford significant new flexibility; work with component suppliers to increase modularity
Resource Fungibility	*Ad hoc* and unsystematic	Standardize procurements	Provide precise specifications for suppliers so they can provide resources and capabilities with guaranteed fungibility
	Limited options	Expand qualified sources	Nurture several viable suppliers so they can provide assured supply and respond quickly to new requirements

	Substitutions costly	Reduce variation and friction	Identify uncontrolled aspects of suppliers' resources that affect processes differently, and control these via improved specifications
Logistical Agility	Inventory-intensive	Reduce inventory requirements	Implement JIT and flow-based processes to shorten replenishment intervals to reduce inventory.
	Slow	Increase responsiveness	Integrate, standardize and automate processes, eliminating unnecessary steps; pre-authorize and maintain open purchasing contracts
	Inflexible	Increase adaptability	Enable more suppliers to receive and easily respond to requests with flexible bids; allow purchasers flexibility in accepting bids that meet most important requirements
	Errorful, inefficient	Improve resource management processes	Improve processes that specify and estimate requirements and improve ability to find, access, ship, track and deliver suitable resources
	Ad hoc or unsystematic	Initiate systematic process	Define measures of resources, capabilities, and process outputs; monitor these and compare with expectations to spot problems early

	Slow to adapt	Accelerate loop closing	Augment key processes with feedback procedures so significant problems trigger adaptive responses
Control of Actions	Imprecise	Refine and improve precision	Set higher quality goals, such as 5-sigma or 6-sigma, to challenge the organization to learn to excel
	Costly	Reduce control costs	Eliminate resource variations that uselessly increase processing costs; optimize processes to simplify, accelerate, and reduce steps; design quality in to reduce test and rework

As Table 6 shows, organizations that aspire to achieving both high-levels of agility and efficiency must take the old idea of interchangeable parts[18] to a new plateau. In the new regimen, parts, products, services, and even whole business units play roles as interchangeable components. Furthermore, we can mix and match them as needed, where needed, to produce desired effects. Hyper-beings excel at composing *ad hoc* holons to accomplish tasks promptly and effectively. "Stand them up, run them, and shut them down" is the motto of the modern agile organization. The only stable, comfortable roles for creatures in this new world are: (1) be a dominant hyper-being in a meaningful arena; or (2) be a superior component competitor that provides a vital resource, capability, product or service. Given that the competitive environment is filled with holarchic entities at multiple levels, the same facts apply for all size competitors. Mediocre performers face a rapidly shrinking habitat.

---

[18] Eli Whitney contracted in 1797 to manufacture 10,000 muskets for the U.S. Army. Until then, each musket was made entirely by a single person, without standardized measurements. Whitney standardized components to make them interchangeable. He also developed processes that enabled many people to assemble many rifles cooperatively and concurrently.

Personal Entrepreneurship: A New Game Requires New Strategy

We'll take a slight digression at this point to consider how all we've learned about hyper-beings bears on us as individuals. Even today, the intelligence of the average human being surpasses that of most organizations in many ways. Humans have evolved through hundreds of thousands of years to a point where every one of us can speak and read natural languages, ride a bicycle on and off roads, and drive vehicles most of the time without accidents. While mundane, these capabilities put us ahead of robots and computers. On the other hand, the machines have caught up to us and overtaken us in many areas where humans reigned supreme for centuries. These areas include hole digging, ball throwing, signal detection, numeric calculation, symbolic computation, chess and checkers playing, text searching, literature indexing and retrieval, auctioneering, and many more. We really are playing in a less exclusive evolutionary arena than was true for our ancestors, and we no longer have as many distinctions or advantages.

Of course, there are large differences among individual people. This means that some individuals may play chess or checkers better than the computers, or that some humans may solve differential equations better than the computer programs Macsyma[19] or Mathematica[20]. These people may remain competitive mathematics problem-solvers for some time. And many pretty good human problem-solvers will remain employable, because they are more versatile than computer programs and more easily integrated into human organizations. So, the evolutionary niche for humans isn't disappearing overnight. Nevertheless, the ability of the average human to thrive, to be comfortable, to extract profit and accumulate wealth will be under increasing pressure, it would seem, as machines become superior at individual skills and hyper-beings continue to shift employment to highly productive, technology-leveraged, components.

This raises questions about what the average person, including you and I, should be doing, and what we should be encouraging our children to do to make each of them valuable in the future economy. No doubt, some of us are sufficiently well off to feel a little smug about such questions, assuming that conditions that enabled us to prosper will always allow similar success to people like us and our kids. I don't think so. I think continuing prosperity for

---

[19] http://www.macsyma.com/
[20] http://www.wolfram.com/

individuals depends on their being able to offer to the economy capabilities that are superior to those available from competing alternatives. Distributed systems make it easy to move jobs from high-cost North America and Europe to low-cost Third World locales. This means that it's no longer sufficient for you to offer to the economy a good quality of service at a price that's consistent with a Western life-style.

Jobs in Information Technology, for example, are moving out of the US to India and other Asian countries. At the same time, most manufacturing jobs have relocated to China. In addition, jobs that traditionally needed human laborers are disappearing, and they won't be replaced by vast numbers of jobs necessarily favoring human performers. The most recent examples of this trend include the self-checkout cashier stations at retail stores. These automata promise to eliminate jobs as effectively as automated teller machines (ATMs) did in the banking industry. Many of the remaining jobs, which just aren't worth automating, will pay wages far below those required to live comfortably. Such jobs will include house cleaners, feeding assistants for nursing homes, manual laborers, child care providers, and the like. While these workers perform essential tasks, they receive little respect, earn paltry wages, and often need to work multiple jobs to survive[46].

Many recent newspaper articles have described the individual stories of how brilliant, hard-working young adults find themselves falling helplessly into these low-paying, expectation-shattering positions. The following excerpt from the *New York Times* [47] is representative:

> Like many other Ivy League students, Rachael M. Roewe had lofty dreams when she entered the Wharton School of the University of Pennsylvania four years ago. She would study economics, then embark on a career analyzing emerging markets.
>
> But the closest she has come to Wall Street since she graduated last May with a bachelor's degree is the MeKong Vietnamese Restaurant and Bar in Greenwich Village, where she works as a waitress on weekday nights and as a bartender on weekends. Last month, she spent her days as a freelance makeup artist at the cosmetics counters of Bergdorf Goodman on Fifth Avenue.
>
> "I'm just doing this for fun," and to help pay the expenses of living in Manhattan, said Ms. Roewe, 22, who grew up in

Burlington, Iowa. She said she had sent out countless résumés and job applications and had even interviewed at a few investment banks, but that she had been told she was either underqualified or overqualified for the few jobs available.

"I went to a really good school and I did all the right things, so what else can you do?" said Ms. Roewe, who says she was the only person in her high school class to attend an Ivy League college. She said she graduated from Wharton with a 3.1 grade-point average. "You realize that just because you went to the best undergraduate business school doesn't guarantee that you will have a job," she said.

Almost half a year after finishing their studies, many graduates of Ivy League and other elite colleges have come to that same realization and, like Ms. Roewe, many are settling for jobs that have little to do with their career goals...

Still, many recent Ivy League graduates remain in a holding pattern. Ms. Roewe said that her Wharton roommate, who also graduated last spring, had a $7-an-hour internship at Universal Studios, and that another former classmate was working at a Gap store.

Margie Tsaousis, 22, who received a political science degree from Vassar College last spring, worked as an unpaid intern at City Hall in San Francisco before being hired as a legal assistant in that city. She is paid $10 an hour and receives no benefits.

As graduates look for high-paying jobs, many may be wondering if the high price of their education was worth it. Ms. Roewe noted that it cost her parents around $100,000 in tuition alone to send her to Wharton for four years. Last week, the College Board reported that it now costs an average of $26,854 a year to attend a four-year private school, including tuition, fees, room and board, up 5.7 percent from last year.

Carlos Sanchez, 22, of Los Angeles said he thought that the bachelor's degree in economics he received from Princeton in May would land him a six-figure job at an investment bank. The reality check came when he met with a recruiter at a temporary agency.

"She asked, 'What is your ideal job?' and I said, 'I'd like to get $100,000 a year.' She said: 'What, are you crazy? It's more like $30,000, and you're going to have to settle with that,'" said Mr. Sanchez, who has moved back in with his parents in Rowland Heights, Calif. ...

Some graduates blame themselves for their predicaments. Sunny Cheung, 22, who graduated this year from the University of California at Berkeley with a degree in computer science, said: "When I got into Berkeley, people told me you'd get a good job for sure, so I didn't think about jobs until my third year in school. By then I started to worry because I had no internship experience."

Mr. Cheung said that by the time he graduated, he had applied to about 50 companies but was only offered four interviews. He said he took the first offer he received: a $7-an-hour internship at an Internet company in San Francisco, with no benefits apart from the free snacks. He said the Berkeley name is somewhat of an added burden.

"My parents were happy about me finally finding a job, but they think the wage is too low." he said. "They weren't happy about a Berkeley grad getting such a low wage."

Ms. Roewe, meanwhile, says she is hopeful about eventually finding a job on Wall Street.

"Our generation thinks that you shouldn't have to do things like wait tables," she said. "My dad worked on a farm and worked an egg-processing job while he was in college, so he tells me I don't want to hear about waitressing. I feel like it isn't the worst thing I could do. Maybe I'd even learn something about hard work."

The history of technology and economics has seen a continuing cycle of innovation and destruction, as Schumpeter famously described[7]. Improving economic conditions, he pointed out, have resulted from a never-ending sequence of innovations that eliminate old jobs but increase productivity and prosperity. We should expect those innovations to continue. However, many of the conditions that, in the past, assured that the spoils of capitalism would be distributed among the vast majority of the population have seemed to be unraveling over the recent past[48, 49]. Barriers to the flow of capital have dropped. Wealth can seek its own jurisdiction. A confluence of rapidly progressing technologies has made the rise of dominant, transnational hyper-beings extremely likely, if not actually inevitable. The supreme competitiveness of these hyper-beings will exaggerate the pull of resources away from the majority and toward a superior and small minority. For these reasons, the expectations of the average person are declining.

I can't foresee whether or how these increasing trends of inequality might be lessened or reversed by political events or new approaches to governance. So I won't assume anything in that regard.

Thus, we come to the question facing each individual: what can I do to make myself valuable, and how can I assure my own prosperity in this challenging new environment? In an abstract way, the answer is simple: offer to supply a superior service that agile organizations want and can employ easily. Practically speaking, however, this is a major challenge to the ways we normally think about getting educated and developing careers. We can no longer find security in learning a body of knowledge, getting a particular degree, or getting a good position at a good company. Things are moving quickly, components are redefined and pitted against one another, and only the best pull ahead. When competition was held back by many barriers, the environment possessed more niches that could support relatively comfortable lives. As we go forward, we need to offer superior services and connect easily to those who want to employ them.

Some traditional careers are partial models for the future. Doctors and lawyers are service providers, and the best specialists have always served the highest bidder. These specialists readily deploy to locations where their services are required, and when needed customers routinely transport the items to be processed to them. These specialized independent service providers illustrate how to succeed: possess unique capabilities and offer to employ them to a broad array of purchasers in a clearly defined market segment.

Not much else about medicine and law is a model for the future, however. These industries are marked by extremely low productivity, are self-regulated, and bar competition in countless ways not generally available to other occupations. Both law and medicine use a good strategy to maintain economic viability: establish a profession that can control its membership and numbers, thereby minimizing competition. In the long run, even this strategy will come under attack, because it severely restricts new sources of supply and significantly slows productivity improvements.

So, how can individuals become highly valued service providers and do so without relying on trade guilds and other quasi-legal means of restricting competition? It seems there is no alternative to becoming really excellent at something the buyers want, and maintaining that excellence over time. Given the ability to digitize most work tasks and intermediate products, few barriers prevent us from offering service to all comers, on a global basis. Thus, in the extreme, each person's success will reflect his or her personal entrepreneurship, the ability to identify a segment of market demand and to develop superior ways to service it. This means each person will need to do well on at least four principal entrepreneurship tasks:

- Do outside-in marketing, to determine what customers desire and value

- Define an innovative or superior product or service that you can deliver to satisfy that desire

- Acquire needed resources and capabilities, and then implement processes to develop and deliver that product or service

- Sell to prospective customers, and out-perform the competition

To people who have acted as self-employed entrepreneurs, independent consultants, contractors, commission-only distributors or sales people, these ideas are neither new nor surprising. To most professionals, salaried employees, and skilled laborers, however, these are strange and frightening portents. Those people grew up believing that there would always be plenty of good jobs waiting for qualified applicants. For years now, the new reality has been dawning: no job lasts forever, and the era of big company loyalty towards employees has clearly ended. Looking ahead, I believe it's likely to get a whole lot harder.

Most of the methods hyper-beings employ to compete at extremely high levels can also work for individuals to improve our personal prospects. Specifically, we too need to excel at efficient thought. We need to understand how to do the four principal entrepreneurial tasks well, and continually improve our performance on these tasks. That means we need to have a good world model of how things work in the market area we're interested in. We need to develop effective plans for achieving the four goals of marketing, product/service design, development-and-delivery, and sales. We need to execute these plans, observe and assess results, and conjecture ways to improve. We need to test those candidate improvements in the competitive arena, and go around the cycle repeatedly. Unless we are extremely successful and can accumulate considerable wealth, we won't be able to get off this wheel until we die or someone else takes care of us. In short, we need to take personal responsibility for choosing some customers, getting their business, and keeping it by outperforming our competitors.

The conclusions just presented don't emanate from any philosophical, political, or moral position. Rather, they seem logically deducible from an understanding of the present and evolving situation. Nobody and nothing is in place to make sure everybody's well-fed, happy, and successful. At the same time, technology, governments, and post-industrial enterprises are all aggressively competing to achieve unsurpassed levels of efficiency through increasing specialization and distributed intelligent integration of components. Nobody is guaranteeing you or me a well-paying, life-long role in any of the new super-competitive winning enterprises. If we want that, we'd better offer the best option they have for something they need.

There's no simple formula for becoming efficient thinkers. We need to practice efficient thought, and this means consciously planning, trying, learning, and starting again. Those tasks apply in every arena. In addition, because we must choose a particular market segment to operate in, we have a lot of specialized world knowledge and specialized skills to acquire. This knowledge acquisition, skill development, and adaptive control of planned behaviors constitute the common work of efficient thinkers.

Meta-intelligence, in addition, can prove crucially important to us. Recall that the tasks of meta-intelligence are to understand our own capabilities and behaviors, to develop plans for improving these, and to determine how to allocate our own scarce resources. Basically, we ought to spend some of our resources trying to determine how to improve our odds of success in ways not already addressed by efficient thought *per se*. Some important meta-intelligence tasks for us follow:

❖ Investigate alternative market areas to scan for attractive new niches

❖ Evaluate opportunities for personal development and undertake the best

❖ Acquire new knowledge and skills that might prove useful in the future

❖ Expose yourself to different cultures and new trends

❖ Study successful products, services, and components to see what you might learn

❖ Try different ways to promote others' awareness of you, your offerings, and your comparative advantages

❖ Keep records of your time, evaluate the value per unit time of various activities, and adjust your behavior to reduce low-value time and increase high-value time

❖ Use resources to cultivate your personal relationships, to improve your health and happiness, and to enjoy the benefits of living

❖ Make an educated guess about how to allocate your time among all the potential competing demands and do that

All of the tasks of meta-intelligence share a perplexing feature: they are difficult to do well and impossible to do perfectly. In fact, none of these comes with a recipe for success. Each task addresses an open-ended challenge, lacking any finite bound or deterministically knowable optimal answer. Nevertheless, when you do one of these tasks well, it usually expands the range of opportunities you consider and improves the odds of your identifying a promising target.

I believe we can all improve our odds by understanding the rules of the game we're playing. This enables us to experiment, learn, and improve our moves. If we want to assure that others pay good prices for our efforts, we must excel at the basic moves of entrepreneurship . The more efficiently we think through those objectives, the more likely we can achieve them. The meta-level moves help us explore a vast space of potential arenas in the hope of acquiring experiences that lead us to greater levels of success in the basic game. Existing social and educational institutions fail entirely to prepare us for these challenges. While we might do very well in life just by blindly following paths others lay out for us, it seems quite unlikely. As an alternative, we can take personal responsibility for guiding our own journey and intelligently attacking the largely predictable challenges that journey entails. This seems prudent and necessary. No promising alternative currently exists.

In sum, the environment is changing for individuals, as much as it is for companies and military organizations. Our familiar, comfortable, slowly changing habitat has been supplanted by a network-centric, dynamic, marketplace for interchangeable components with specialized capabilities. Profit margins earned by suppliers of interchangeable components approach nil. Assuming we personally aspire to a substantially better return on our personal capital, we'd better get busy learning to become the best deliverers on Earth of highly prized services. Even if we come up slightly short of that goal, our position will have many advantages over positions open to the ignorantly complacent.

Jumping Off the Evolutionary Tree

As we all know, life on Earth has progressed for billions of years according to the laws of biology, genetics, and natural selection. Basically, the environment has tested the fitness of candidate beings, and those belonging to well-adapted species out-competed others operating in the same niches. The successful ones reproduced more prolifically and thereby won the right to continuing playing the game.

Richard Dawkins was the first to point out that the evolutionary process did a jump shift from the biological space to the space of ideas, where *memes* play the same role as genes play in the genetic arena.[50] Since people have become the dominant species on Earth, they have become hosts for concepts, ideas, and beliefs that jump from them much the way biological organisms host genes, viruses and other genetic material. Memes are the unitary items that embody individual beliefs. Of course, memes are just abstractions, disembodied information. We can think of these as bits, and this is another example of a shift of the world's processes from moving molecules to moving bits. Bits control what people believe and how they behave. With modern technologies of global communication, memes can infect the world rapidly and rabidly. For good or ill, natural selection has begun to operate in the fast-paced arena of communicable ideas.

Two other authors have also made important contributions to our ability to see how ideas and information actually control the behaviors of human civilization. Leslie White [51] was an early scholar of culture who pointed out that money and resources flow to support those ideas that capture the minds and imaginations of people. Mutually reinforcing ideas, such as "God" and "the afterlife," or "freedom" and "liberty," or "the evil empire" and "nuclear deterrence," gain much from the fact that they dovetail and support one another. As ideas take root among entire cultures, those cultures funnel resources to the institutions and groups that promote and defend those ideas. Thus, concepts control cultures and strongly determine the flow of resources. White pointed out to understand culture you must first abstract the people out of the picture. Then, you can see more easily which ideas are garnering the big resources.

In his book *Darwin among the Machines*, George Dyson [52] traces the evolution of information processing capabilities, through animals, humans, and then computers and networks. He explains clearly how and why natural selection moves faster when it gains a foothold in the environment of bits rather than molecules. He points out how the recent progress in computing and networking has created a fertile, albeit artificial, field for natural selection to operate. He anticipates that machine-based evolution will proceed at unprecedented rates, leading to a machine-based supremacy operating in the sphere of information.

I have shown in this book how these insights combine with practical, everyday organizational behavior. Three facts make the rise of hyper-beings predictable:

- Organizations perform most productive work and control most resources.

- Advances in distributed intelligent systems enable leading organizations to improve and scale up dramatically.

- Traditional barriers to size and power, such as nationalism and protectionism, have succumbed to the conceptual and economic dominance of globalism.

These lines of reasoning all imply that hyper-beings will evolve rapidly. Further, because they are competing in a world where bits largely determine and control reality, natural selection will encourage their rise to dominant positions. Concepts and memes travel the world at the speed of light. Increasingly, hyper-beings process these ideas more completely, more effectively, and more rapidly than any other creatures can. Bits control money, power, and influence. Capital moves at the speed of light, from one account to another, from one nation to another, chasing the highest possible returns. Those highest returns increasingly result from efficient thought and agile configuration, the province of hyper-beings.

For these reasons, we see that the new superior beings have jumped off the evolutionary tree. The new dominant species doesn't descend from animals, hominids, and *homo sapiens*. The new species is a hybrid that incorporates a variety of powerful capabilities. These capabilities include:

> ➢ human brains and human muscles;

> ➢ computer-based brains and robotic effectors;

> ➢ rapidly expanding networks that sense and monitor activities at all scales, everywhere, around the clock;

> ➢ multiple natural and artificial language systems, enabling humans and machines to understand and operate upon significant information;

> ➢ vast communication networks enabling ever increasing numbers of humans and machines to collaborate in real time.

The superior beings that emerge to integrate and combine these advantages will dominate large niches indeed. We humans have few attractive options. We can find a role functioning within them, invent a symbiotic relationship that makes cooperating with them appealing, or find a tiny niche for ourselves that's outside their ecosystem.

The direction of progress is clear. People and systems are going to become increasingly networked, virtual, organized, collaborative, efficient, and effective. The owners and key employees of these successful giants should reap terrific rewards. These organizations will think efficiently and act with agility. This will create enhanced opportunities for people to progress based on the merit of their contributions. The organizations, attuned to efficient thinking and continuous improvement, will increasingly base performance reviews on an objective basis. The search for valid ideas will lead to increased investments in research and rewards for innovative thinkers and empiricists. Transnational operations will lead to increased workplace diversity. It will expand opportunities to travel to foreign cultures and work within many different people. The increasingly effective exploitation of talent and capability, supported by light-speed computing and communication, should produce a new era of innovation, profits, and wealth.

Asymmetries between the advanced and the primitive, between the hyper-beings and the dispossessed, between the affluent and the poor will grow more extreme. For dominant forces, such as the US military, this presents a "good news, bad news" situation. First, heightened asymmetries will increase discord, making it likely that challenges to the hegemony of the dominant players will arise in more places, more often. Terrorists, for example, will learn to work around our advantages, and challenges our vulnerabilities. They will attack the weak, unprotected underbelly of the advanced world, including the foundations for freedom of movement, safety of investment, and 24x7 computing and communications.

Military organizations will need to learn to use their potential capabilities for global, wide-scale, collaboration to improve their ability to detect, monitor, and neutralize such threats. Rather than continuing to evolve primarily as organizations that can mass forces against national state enemies, they will need to learn how to become global "security maintenance" organizations, that resemble police and disease control organizations. Enemies will arise that emphasize features such as dispersion, low-technology, and mobility to neutralize the US ability to destroy any significant stationary target. This means our own forces will need to evolve into an even more dispersed, mobile, agile, and fast acting swarm.

Whether we focus on our selves, from the point of view of maximizing our personal capital, or on our business, our military, our nation, or some other organization of interest, our concerns and agendas will need to address several central themes. To harness the forces driving the emergence of hyper-beings most effectively, we have identified and discussed eight imperatives:

1. **Get Networked, Go Virtual**

2. **Organize, Cooperate, Communicate**

3. **Think Efficiently**

4. **Act Effectively**

5. **Shape the Competitive Environment**

6. **Exploit Technology**

7. **Leverage Human Potential**

8. **Continually Improve, Adapt and Evolve Yourself**

Efficient thought and agile action allow new superior organizations to get huge bang for the buck. They create better ideas about what's worth doing. They hit the target faster and more accurately than their competitors. They can bring more actors onto the playing field where advantageous to support their efforts. Today's technology allows modern organizations to connect and cooperate with anyone on the face of the Earth. Walls around teams, businesses or even countries no longer provide protection or advantage. The Internet and other telecommunications vault over those walls effortlessly.

Practitioners of efficient thought continuously employ and improve their superior knowledge, which they use for modeling how things work, how to plan effective missions, and how to analyze results. Technology makes it possible for us to provide resources at the exact location at the exact time they're required. We can coordinate how events are timed and synchronized across vast regions of space. We can employ our extensive resources with their capabilities for sensing, analysis, problem-solving and control to out-compete all comers. With these resources, for example, we can determine the best ways, locations, times and instruments to employ to delight customers or starve competitors. We can shape the competitive environment by thinking faster than our opponents, using resources more effectively, and deriving greater profits from our superior efficiency and agility.

Every opportunity we can identify, at least for some time, is open to all interested competitors. The best-of breed-hyper-beings will excel at exploiting the capabilities of IT to amplify and extend their potential. They will also excel at appreciating, cultivating, and rewarding various human capabilities. Human capacity for innovation, analytical perspicacity, insight and sound judgment can constitute a significant competitive advantage.

But no hyper-being can afford sloppy, informal, or biased thinking. Only continuous improvement guarantees excellence. CI demands that we look objectively at why disappointing and surprising results occur. It demands that we determine which of our beliefs and behavior patterns requiring changing and that we implement those changes effectively.

Life among the hyper-beings demands cunning and speed. This "game" has no finish line. We and our organizations get a new chance each day, through natural selection, to win an option to play again tomorrow. Eventually, mediocre performers fall behind and lose everything. No safety net exists to assure them a reasonably comfortable booby prize. The only prudent thing for us to do is to race into the future, seeking a rewarding position, as a valued supplier of needed capabilities aboard one of the biggest, fiercest, most dominant creatures ever imagined: a 21st-century hyper-being.

7. Summary and Conclusions

I warned you that I might sound a bit strident. I am concerned, and I am excited. I see greater opportunity for people to assemble powerful organizations than most of us can imagine. This means we might be on the threshold of a new age of productivity, creativity, and social welfare. Each of us and our children and grandchildren might participate in this revolution in various ways, hopefully benefiting from the new wealth created.

Several trends have come together to create a platform on which this new productivity can be assembled and delivered. We have advances across the board in information technologies, and these are continuing to accelerate. Our computers are getting smaller and faster. We can store almost infinite amounts of information in tiny volumes. We can communicate incredibly fast, and the speed, quality, and availability of communications are increasing at great rates. We have modeled huge areas of natural and artificial materials, processes, and phenomena. Our models let us predict, explain and control many things. We can plan for a wide variety of operations and use adaptive control processes to achieve predicted results, with high confidence as well as high accuracy.

There are many ways in which our knowledge is incomplete or imperfect, but we have learned meta-processes that enable us to improve it. We can identify errors and omissions and conjecture new ideas to address them. We can experiment scientifically to validate innovations, ranging from concepts to new products. We have learned how to learn and improve continuously. Pursuing these methods with discipline can assure that the best among us pull ahead even further.

We don't currently do a very good job educating people about the essential processes that contribute to the new possibilities of superiority. We still emphasize teaching people facts and behavior, rather than efficient thought and innovation. Our educational system lags behind the changes being wrought by the fast pace of technology and organizational evolution. Many people over the last decade have independently discovered that (1) their personal success didn't seem to depend on what they were learning in school and (2) that doing well in school might not lead anywhere for them. We will need to change the focus of our teaching and educational concepts to deliver more value to the average customer/student. The average person needs to learn how to develop a world-class capability that can be delivered to global customers who value it. Of course, that means the person needs to learn the basic skills of entrepreneurship, some specialized knowledge in particular domains of application, and the meta-processes of learning and continuous improvement. For those who master these skills, life should be extremely rewarding.

The modern world is the playing field for distributed intelligent systems. These systems align with dominant businesses, governments, militaries and a few other organizations. Their aspirations impel them to grow bigger and more dominant. Meanwhile, traditional barriers to rampant growth have fallen, removing most of the limiting factors. As a consequence, our contemporary environment permits these systems to expand to unprecedented scale, with unparallel capacity. Competition encourages them to improve, and natural selection assures that the best will gain market share, diminish competitors, and ultimately achieve supremacy. Just as water flows downhill and floods depressions to form lakes, technology-enhanced superiority produces growth, efficiency and dominance of various niches.

We stand today at an inflection point in human history. The rate of improvement in the best organizations is accelerating dramatically as they learn to harness information technology, discipline their processes, and adopt objective approaches to continuous improvement. In what will seem like the blink of eye to people in the next century, hyper-beings will rise up, master the knowledge and processes required, exploit the technology effectively, and establish hegemonies that will persist for decades or centuries.

Notes

1. Koestler, A., *The Ghost in the Machine*. 1967, London: Arkana.

2. Friedman, T., *The Lexus and the Olive Tree: Understanding Globalization*. 2000, New York: Anchor.

3. Lux, T. and M. Marchesi, *Scaling and criticality in a stochastic multi-agent model of a financial market*. Nature, 1999. **397**: p. 498-500.

4. Hammer, M., *The Agenda: What every business must do to dominate the decade*. 2001, New York: Crown Business.

5. Schumpeter, J.A., *The Theory of Economic Development*. 1934, Cambridge, MA: Harvard Univ. Press.

6. Schumpeter, J.A., *The creative response in economic history*. Journal of Economic History, 1947: p. 149-159.

7. Schumpeter, J.A., *History of Economic Analysis*. 1954, New York: Oxford University Press.

8. Lakatos, I., *Proofs and Refutations: The Logic of Mathematical Discoveries*. 1976, New York: Cambridge University Press.

9. Hayes-Roth, F., P. Klahr, and D.J. Mostow, *Knowledge acquisition, knowledge programming, and knowledge refinement*, in *Expert Systems: Techniques, Tools and Applications*, P. Klahr and D.A. Waterman, Editors. 1986, Addison Wesley: Reading, MA. p. 310-349.

10. Hayes-Roth, F., P. Klahr, and D.J. Mostow, *Advice-taking and knowledge refinement: An iterative view of skill acquisition*, in *Skill Acquisition and Development*, J.R. Anderson, Editor. 1981, Erlbaum Associates: Hillsdale, NJ.

11. Munkvold, B.E., *Implementing Collaboration Technologies in Industry*. 2003, New York: Springer-Verlag.

12. Bateson, G., *Steps to an ecology of mind*. 1972, New York: Ballantine Books.

13. Ashby, W.R., *An Introduction to Cybernetics*. 1956, London: Chapman & Hall.

14.   Hayes-Roth, B., *Intelligent Control.* Artificial Intelligence, 1993.
        59(1-2): p. 213-220.

15.   Hayes-Roth, B. and F. Hayes-Roth, *A cognitive model of planning.*
        Cognitive Science, 1979. **3**: p. 275-310.

16.   Hayes-Roth, F. and V.R. Lesser. *Focus of attention in the Hearsay-II
        system.* in *Fifth Intl. JCAI.* 1976. Cambridge, MA.

17.   Hayes-Roth, B., *A Blackboard Architecture for Control.* Artificial
        Intelligence, 1985. **26**: p. 251-321.

18.   Maslow, A., *Motivation and Personality.* 2nd ed. 1970, New York:
        Harper & Row.

19.   Licklider, J.C.R., *Man-Computer Symbiosis.* IRE Transactions on
        Human Factors in Electronics, 1960. **HFE-1**: p. 4-11.

20.   Licklider, J.C.R. and R.W. Taylor, *The Computer as a
        Communication Device.* Science and Technology, 1968.

21.   Waldrop, M.M., *The Dream Machine: J.C.R. Licklider and the
        Revolution That Made Computing Personal.* 2002, New York:
        Penguin.

22.   Smith, H. and P. Fingar, *Business Process Management (BPM): The
        Third Wave.* 2003, Tampa, FL: Meghan-Kiffer Press.

23.   Rummler, G.A. and A.P. Brache, *Improving Performance: How to
        Manage the White Space in the Organization Chart.* 2nd ed. 1995,
        San Francisco: Jossey-Bass.

24.   Hinds, P.J. and S. Kiesler, eds. *Distributed Work.* 2002, MIT Press:
        Cambridge, MA.

25.   Lipnack, J.S., J., *Virtual Teams: People Working Across Boundaries
        with Technology.* 2000, New York: John Wiley and Sons.

26.   Albus, J.S. and A.M. Meystel, *Intelligent Systems: Architecture,
        Design, Control.* 2001, New York: Wiley-Interscience.

27.   Albus, J.S., *The NIST real-time control system (RCS): an approach to
        intelligent systems research.* Journal of Experimental & Theoretical
        Artificial Intelligence, 1997. **9**(2/3): p. 147-156.

28.   Albus, J.S., H.G. McCain, and R. Lumia, *NASA/NBS Standard Reference Model for Telerobot Control System Architecture (NASREM)*. 1989, National Institute of Standards and Technology: Gaithersburg, MD.

29.   Hayes-Roth, F., et al., *ABE: A cooperative operating system and development environment*, in *AI Tools and Techniques*, M. Richer, Editor. 1989, Ablex Publishing: Norwood, NJ. p. 323-355.

30.   Erman, L.D., J.S. Lark, and F. Hayes-Roth, *ABE: An environment for engineering intelligent systems*. IEEE Transactions on Software Engineering, 1988. **14**(12).

31.   Hayes-Roth, F., et al., *ABE: A cooperative operating system and development environment*, in *Readings in Distributed Artificial Intelligence*, A. Bond and L. Gasser, Editors. 1988, Morgan Kaufmann. p. 457-488.

32.   Hayes-Roth, F., et al. *Tools and Methods for Developing Distributed Intelligent Control and Management (DICAM) Application Systems*. in *Joint Services Guidance and Control Committee (JSGCC) Software Initiative Workshop*. 1992. Vail, CO: Meridian.

33.   Lark, J.S., et al., *Architecture for composing computational modules uniformly across diverse developmental frameworks*. 1990, Teknowledge: Palo Alto, CA.

34.   Hayes-Roth, F., et al. *Distributed Intelligent Control and Management: Concepts, methods and tools for developing DICAM applications*. in *SEKE 92: Fourth International Conference on Software Engineering and Knowledge Engineering*. 1992. Capri, Italy: IEEE.

35.   Hayes-Roth, F., et al. *Distributed Intelligent Control and Management (DICAM) Applications and Support for Semi-Automated Development*. in *AAAI-92 Workshop on Automating Software Development*. 1992. San Jose, CA: AAAI.

36.   Hayes-Roth, F., et al. *Domain-Specific Software Architectures: Distributed Intelligent Control and Management*. in *IEEE Symposium on Computer-Aided Control System Design*. 1992. Napa, CA: IEEE.

37.   Hayes-Roth, F., *Architecture-Based Acquisition and Development of Software: Guidelines and Recommendations from the ARPA Domain-*

Specific Software Architecture (DSSA) Program. 1994, Teknowledge Federal Systems.

38.   Simon, H.A., *The Sciences of the Artificial (3rd ed.).* 1996, Cambridge, MA: MIT Press.

39.   Dawkins, R., *The Blind Watchmaker.* 1987, New York: Norton.

40.   Alberts, D.S., J.J. Garstka, and F.P. Stein, *Network Centric Warfare: Developing and Leveraging Information Superiority.* 2nd ed. 2002, Washington, D.C.: Office of the Secretary of Defense (ASD/C3I/CCRP).

41.   Shiller, R.J., *The New Financial Order: Risk in the 21st Century.* 2003, Princeton, NJ: Princeton Univ. Press.

42.   Oakland, J.S., *TQM: Text with Cases.* 3rd ed. 2003, Newton, MA: Butterworth-Heinemann.

43.   ReVelle, J.B., *The QFD Handbook.* 1998, New York: Wiley.

44.   Marash, S.A., P. Berman, and M. Flynn, *Fusion Management: Harnessing the Power of Six Sigma, Lean, ISO 9001:2000, Malcolm Baldridge, TQM and Other Quality Breakthroughs of the Past Century.* 2003, Milwaukee: American Society for Quality.

45.   Premack, D., *Reversibility of the reinforcement relationship.* Science, 1962. **136**: p. 255-257.

46.   Ehrenreich, B., *Nickel and Dimed: On (Not) Getting By in America.* 2001, Henry Holt: New York.

47.   Wu, A., *A Tight Job Market Dampens Ivy League Hopes*, in *The New York Times*. 2003.

48.   Phillips, K., *Wealth and Democracy.* 2002, New York: Broadway Books.

49.   Krugman, P., *The Great Unraveling: Losing Our Way in the New Century.* 2003, New York: Norton.

50.   Dawkins, R., *The Selfish Gene.* 1990, Oxford: Oxford Press.

51.   White, L.A., *The Science of Culture: A Study of Man and Civilization.* 1969, New York: Farrar, Straus and Giroux.

52. Dyson, G.B., *Darwin among the Machines: The evolution of global intelligence.* 1997, Reading, MA: Perseus.

Index

India, 16, 22, 165
Inference, 1, 11, 45, 47, 48
Information Age, 34
Information and communication
technology (ICT), 85
Information qualities, 34, 65, 72
Information sharing, 6, 33, 115
Information, Production of, 25
Information-superior organizations, 2, 6,
9, 24, 25, 27, 31, 32, 33, 37, 44, 52, 67,
82, 126, 133, 176
Infrastructure, Critical, 28
Innovation, 1, 13, 21, 22, 23, 25, 27, 29,
33, 90, 91, 92, 105, 121, 132, 144, 149,
167, 174, 176, 178
Instant messaging (IM), 10, 20, 81
Intel Corp., 22, 23
Intelligence, ix, x, 5, 7, 34, 37, 61, 68, 76,
78, 86, 90, 92, 98, 101, 105, 120, 125,
133, 146, 164, 170, 171, 184
Intelligence analysis, 61, 183
Intelligent beings, 52, 58, 59, 79, 80, 81,
86
Intelligent control, 73, 74, 95, 96, 97, 98,
99, 105, 113, 114, 122
Intelligent controller, 95, 97, 98, 99
Intelligent systems, xi, 4, 31, 51, 52, 53,
60, 86, 90, 91, 92, 93, 94, 95, 100, 101,
105, 106, 110, 114, 126, 130, 133, 134,
181, 182
Intenet Engineering Task Force (IETF), 11
Interfaces, 110, 112, 119, 127, 138, 142,
146, 152
Internet, x, 4, 5, 6, 9, 10, 11, 20, 24, 28,
74, 123, 131, 139, 155, 167, 176
Interpretation, 133
Invention, ix, 19, 24, 25, 41, 174
Iran, 71
Iraq, 28, 132

J

Joint and Coalition Operations, 75, 133,
146, 154
Justification, 36
Just-in-time (JIT) systems, 121, 125, 162

K

Kansas, 9, 10
Keep it simple stupid (KISS), 73
Kereitsu, 12
Klahr, Phil, 56, 180
Know-how, 1, 7, 12, 23, 25, 34, 37
Knowledge, 1, 13, 14, 19, 23, 24, 25, 27,
29, 32, 33, 34, 35, 37, 40, 41, 43, 46,
49, 51, 54, 56, 58, 59, 60, 61, 67, 69,
76, 81, 90, 91, 92, 93, 94, 97, 100, 105,
106, 113, 115, 119, 120, 121, 122, 126,
129, 130, 133, 135, 145, 146, 147, 148,
150, 168, 170, 171, 178, 179, 180, 182
Knowledge management, 100, 150
Knowledge, Informal, 23
Knowledge, Scientific, 23
Koestler, Arthur, 3, 12, 110, 180
Korea, South, 22

L

La Brea Tar Pits, xi
Labor, 1, 12, 16, 17, 21, 26, 27, 45, 136
Labor Costs, 12
Labor, Power of, 16
Labor, Underutilization of, 17
Lakatos, Imre, 55, 180
Langston, Marv, ix
Langston, Marv
Bold Ideas group, ix
Languages, 11, 13, 102, 104, 118, 133,
134, 135, 141, 147, 149, 155, 156, 161,
164, 174
Larsen, Gary, 78
Latin America, 17
Law of Requisite Variety, 93
Lean operations, 14
Learning, 33, 54, 56, 58, 85, 134
Lesser, Victor, 113, 181
Licklider, J. C. R., 98, 181
Life forms, ix, 4, 29
Life forms, Hybrid, 29
Linux, 28
Logistics, 121, 139, 160, 162
Luggage, lost, 38, 39, 42

Printed in the United States
151244LV00001B/1/A